Space and Spirit

THE HUMANIST LIBRARY

Wheelwright & Regnery Co.
23 East 26th Street, New York 10, N. Y.
DISTRIBUTORS

THE HUMANIST LIBRARY

SIR EDMUND WHITTAKER, F. R. S.

Space and Spirit

THEORIES OF THE UNIVERSE AND THE
ARGUMENTS FOR THE EXISTENCE OF GOD

1948

HENRY REGNERY COMPANY

HINSDALE, ILLINOIS

Production and design by Edit, Inc., Chicago

Preface

THE following pages represent the substance of Donnellan lectures delivered in June, 1946, in Trinity College, Dublin. My grateful thanks are offered to the Provost and Fellows for the honor conferred by their appointment of me as Donnellan lecturer, and for the opportunity thus afforded of attempting to throw some new light on a very old problem.

E. T. W.

The University of Edinburgh, Scotland

Contents

Space and Spirit

1
How this book came to be written

THE most famous arguments for the existence of God are the *Five Ways,* as they are called, of St. Thomas Aquinas, which take as their starting-point the external material world, and lead by different sequences of thought to Deity. Some time ago a friend of mine, a clergyman, told me of a young agnostic who had come to him for instruction. The inquirer was of excellent intellectual quality, and had taken a university degree in physics. My friend had put before him St. Thomas' Five Ways, and had found that they made no impression. I asked if this was because the inquirer did not accept the preliminary assumptions from which St. Thomas' proofs started, and learned that this was indeed the difficulty. "But," said my friend, "the assumptions are true." "Whether they are true or not," I replied, "is not the question: the question is whether the inquirer accepts them, for unless he is willing to assume them as true it is useless to take up his time in drawing deductions from them."

I have reproduced this conversation because it illustrates a state of things which seems to call for some attention. The Five Ways start from our knowledge of the same universe that furnishes the subject-matter of modern physics; their purpose is to lift up the mind from nature to God. Since the thirteenth century, when St. Thomas wrote, there have been profound changes in the conception of the material world, which have had repercussions on the philosophy of physics; fundamental notions such as those of matter, causality, and design have taken new forms, and consequently there have been changes in the status and interpretation of the initial assumptions from which his arguments proceed. We may be assured that, if he were alive now, he would start from the science of Nature as we know it, a science that is immensely richer than was dreamt of in his day, and that he would show how it could be gathered into the framework of divine knowledge.

My object is to give some account of the history of the problem and to discuss the position as it stands today.

2

Jews and Stoics

St. Thomas was, of course, not the first writer to discern in natural phenomena a foundation for reasoning about God. The principle that the external world bears witness to

Him is the theme of much superb poetry in the Old Testament;[1] and in the Judaism of the age immediately preceding the Christian era, it was taught[2] that the fact of the existence of God, and some understanding of His character, may be inferred from our experience of the world by the light of reason alone, without the aid of revelation. The possibility of this *Natural Theology,* as it is called, was restated by St. Paul in his addresses at Lystra[3] and Athens[4] and in his letter to the Romans,[5] and has been accepted in all ages by Christians generally.[6]

These ideas, however, were not peculiar to the peoples of the Bible; they were prominent also in some of the pagan philosophies of the ancient world, especially in that of the Stoics;[7] and indeed it has been the Stoic, rather than the Jewish, manner of treating the subject that has been most generally followed by medieval and modern Christian writers.

1 *Cf. e.g.* Job, Chs. 37 to 41; Psalms 8, 19, 104

2 *Cf. Wisdom* XIII: 5, 8, 9

3 Acts xiv. 15–17 4 Acts xvii. 24–28 5 Romans i. 30

6 In the words of the Vatican Council of 1870: *Eadem sancta mater Ecclesia tenet et docet, Deum, rerum omnium principium et finem, naturali humanae rationis lumine e rebus creatis certo cognosci posse.* Denzinger, *Enchiridion,* No. 1785.

7 The Stoics are specially considered here on account of their importance at the time when Christianity came on the scene, and also because Natural Theology reached its highest development in Stoicism as compared with the other philosophical schools. Needless to say, their teaching was to a considerable extent borrowed from their predecessors; to discuss its indebtedness would take us too far afield, but mention should be made of the fundamental treatment of Natural Theology by Plato in the tenth book of the *Laws.*

The Stoic system had been founded about three hundred years before the Christian era by Zeno, an Athenian philosopher originally from Cyprus; but the form in which it came into contact with the early Christian church was the Stoicism of the later or Roman period, as expounded for instance in the second book of Cicero's work, *Of the Nature of the Gods.*[8] It aimed at explaining all the phenomena of the material world by ultimate causes, and thus obtaining a doctrine of the formation of the universe and a philosophical conception of its scource, namely, Deity; the term κόσμος indeed was used sometimes simply of order, sometimes of the ordered totality of things, and sometimes of God. "That there are Gods," says the Stoic Balbus in Cicero,[9] "needs no proof"; nevertheless he gave many proofs.

The most important of these was based on the observed rational order in the world. "Recall to thy recollection this alternative," says Marcus Aurelius,[10] "either there is providence, or else a fortuitous concurrence of atoms; remember the arguments by which it has been proved that the world is a kind of political community." "Either it is a well-arranged universe," he adds,[11] "or a chaos huddled together. Can order subsisting in yourself be compatible with disorder

[8] It was developed in the Roman imperial age by Seneca (3–65 A.D.), Epictetus (*flor.* 94 A.D.), and the emperor Marcus Aurelius (121–180 A.D.). The different presentations were by no means concordant even on fundamental matters, *e.g.,* Epictetus was a theist while Aurelius was, in the main, a pantheist.

[9] *De Natura Deorum* II 2

[10] *Meditations* IV 3

[11] *ibid.* IV 27

in the All?" And Cicero's Balbus remarks,[12] "He who believes [the fortuitous explanation] possible, may as well believe, that if a great quantity of the one-and-twenty letters, composed either of gold or any other matter, were thrown upon the ground, they would fall into such order as legibly to form the *Annals* of Ennius."

The vivid sense of order in the material world, which is found throughout Stoic literature, is the more striking when it is remembered that, except for the numerical relations of harmony in music which had been discovered by Pythagoras, the Stoics knew nothing of the vast network of mathematical relations which to our ideas constitute the outstanding evidence of universal order. Be that as it may, they never doubted the existence of a reign of law, and argued that it implies intelligence or mind; so that from the harmonious relations recognizable in the cosmos it is right to infer the existence of a foreseeing providence, a divine Reason operative in the world. In the words of Cleanthes' *Hymn to Zeus,* "Thee doth all this universe that circles round the earth obey, moving whithersoever thou guidest it, and being willingly governed by thee."

The notion of government with a definite purpose in view was prominent in the Stoic doctrine. "What, then, after all, is the world?" asked Epictetus.[13] "Hath it no Governor? How is it possible, when neither a city nor a house can

[12] *De Natura Deorum* II 37

[13] *Discourses* II 15

remain ever so short a time, without some one to govern and take care of it, that this vast and beautiful system should be administered in a fortuitous and disorderly manner?" Another idea which played a great part in the subsequent development, that of *chains of causation,* is also in some measure traceable to the same school. "In the series of things," wrote Marcus Aurelius,[14] "those which follow are always aptly fitted to those which have gone before; for this series is not like a mere enumeration of disjointed things, but it has a rational connection."

The Stoic proofs of the existence of Deity were not specially bound up with the distinctive Stoic teaching about the form and origin of the material universe (which therefore need not be considered here); the assumptions about order, purpose, and causality, from which the arguments started, would have been acceptable to almost any thinker until comparatively recent times, and on this account could be taken over with little or no change into the scheme which St. Thomas framed more than a thousand years later.

The apologetic treatises of the early Christians often show marked Stoic influences, particularly when the writer was a converted philosopher. Athenagoras of Athens, in embracing Christianity, carried over into his new faith much of the attitude to Nature that he had acquired in earlier life. "We have," he wrote,[15] "such incentives to piety in the

[14] *Meditations* IV 45

[15] *Plea of Athenagoras for the Christians* IV. This work is dated about 177 A.D.

established order, the universal harmony, the magnitude, the color, the form, the arrangement of the world," and [16] "If the world is an instrument in tune, and moving in well-measured time, I adore the Being who gave its harmony, and strikes its notes, and sings the accordant strain." [17]

3
The harm done by Neoplatonism

Nevertheless, for a thousand years, from the fourth century to the thirteenth, the Stoic type of apologetic was—shall we say—unfashionable. The cause of this phenomenon must now be inquired into.

The emergence of the Church from the catacombs brought Christianity into closer contact with the philosophy of the Greco-Roman world at a time when that philosophy was undergoing a profound change. Stoicism ceased to be a living force after the end of the second century, and was replaced in the third by Neoplatonism, which reigned without a serious rival until the end of classical paganism.

Honoring Plato as the supreme master, the Neoplatonists supplemented his doctrines by appropriating whatever ap-

[16] *ibid.* XVI

[17] On the other hand, the earliest works of Christian apologetics now extant, namely those of St. Justin Martyr, which were written about 150 A.D., do not refer to the idea that an assurance of God may be derived from a study of Nature; indeed St. Justin evidently held that the sole source of divine knowledge was revelation, and he devoted some effort to proving the curious theory that such elements of truth as were to be found in the teachings of the Academy had been borrowed by Plato from Moses; *cf.* St. Justin, *First Apology,* Chs. 59, 60.

peared to them to be of value in the teaching of Aristotle and (to some extent) of the Stoics,[1] so as to comprehend in a unified system the best of Hellenic thought; and this they offered to mankind in the spirit of the oriental mystery-religions, as a message of salvation to the individual soul. It is most logically and intelligibly set forth in the writings of its last great exponent, Proclus, who taught at Athens in the fifth century. Proclus, who was the most eminent mathematician of his day, arranged the doctrines of Neoplatonism in an orderly sequence of 211 propositions,[2] proved in the syllogistic manner of Euclidean geometry; in spite of much that was essentially mystical and some things that are still obscure in the subject-matter, it may be said that no form of religion has ever been more clearly expounded.

The transition from Stoicism to Neoplatonism had particularly significant effects as regards natural philosophy. The Stoics, more than any other school, had recognized the reign of law in Nature and had attached a high importance to scientific investigation. To the Neoplatonists, on the other hand, the material world was the lowest and vilest element in the scheme of things, and matter was a cause and embodiment of evil; their greatest teacher Plotinus[3] (so we are informed by his disciple Porphyry) blushed because he had a body. So far as they took any notice of natural knowledge,[4]

[1] But not of the Epicureans; and of course they opposed the Stoic materialism.

[2] Στοιχείωσις Θεολογική, *The Elements of Theology*

[3] Born in Egypt in 204 or 205 A.D.

[4] Proclus wrote an *Elements of Physics.*

they followed Aristotle; but their supramundane metaphysical system, in which no historical event could have any significance, left empirical knowledge aside, and focused attention entirely on the One, the superessential supreme principle, and its various emanations. Incidentally, it starved mathematics by depriving it of any contact with experimental science, and created an intellectual atmosphere in which scientific research of every kind was abandoned. For minds of a certain type, however, Neoplatonism has always had a powerful attraction; and there have even been instances in modern times of philosophers who have renounced in its favor the Christian faith in which they had been brought up. But in the early centuries the philosophy of Plotinus and Proclus was never really a dangerous antagonist to Christianity, which was grounded on a historical revelation appealing to the philosopher and the common man alike, and which moreover had the immense advantage of a world-wide organized body with a definite membership.

While to outward appearances the triumph of Christianity was complete, in the more subtle domain of the intellect the victory was not at all one-sided. Neoplatonism affected in a very high degree the development of Christian philosophy, and in particular the Christian attitude to empirical science. This came about in two ways. The first was the influence of St. Augustine, who has acknowledged both in the *Confessions* and in the *City of God*[5] the help he had

[5] *Confessions* VII; *City of God* X

received from the writings of Plotinus at the greatest crisis of his spiritual life; from them was derived the conviction, which he transmitted to the succeeding generations of many centuries, that the only type of knowledge to be desired was knowledge of God and the soul, and that no profit was to be had from investigating the realm of Nature.

The second way was associated with one of the most remarkable incidents in the history of Christian thought. Early in the sixth century an unknown admirer of Proclus produced a number of works which he ascribed to the authorship of Dionysius the Areopagite, the Athenian who was converted by St. Paul,[6] but which consisted essentially of Neoplatonic philosophy covered with a veneer of Christian terminology. The deception was successful, the writings being almost universally accepted as genuine; they were translated into Syriac almost immediately, and into Latin by the Irish scholar John Scotus Erigena in the ninth century, after which they became well known in the West. St. Thomas certainly studied them closely. Although the fraudulent character of the ascription has long been recognized, the intrinsic quality of the work has saved it from contempt; and in the present century a distinguished Quaker scholar,[7] in a treatise on mystical religion, has devoted a sympathetic chapter to the pseudo-Dionysius, and given him a place of honor in the succession of Christian mystics.

---

[6] Acts xvii. 34

[7] Professor Rufus M. Jones, *Studies in Mystical Religion,* Ch. VI

4
St. Anselm's ontological proof

The infusion of Neoplatonist ideas into the Christian outlook had important consequences as regards the attitude of the churchmen toward natural philosophy. For a thousand years, from Plotinus to the revival of Aristotelianism under St. Albert the Great and St. Thomas, the recognition of God through His revelation in Nature was neglected in comparison with other approaches to theology, and the study of empirical science received but little attention. In the earlier Middle Ages the most famous attempt to establish the existence of God by pure reason was that of St. Anselm,[1] generally known as the ontological proof.[2] This makes no reference to the external world of Nature; the argument is, in brief, that (as Plato had shown in his doctrine of Ideas) the concepts of absolute truth, absolute goodness, absolute justice, and so on, are not mere figments of the mind, but have a reality of their own, which is the foundation of the truth of general propositions; they were the *noumena,* of which all individual things were the *phenomena.* These must be referred to a Being who embodies them, a Being who is to Ideas what Ideas are to phenomena, a Being "than whom nothing more perfect can be conceived." It has often been objected that St. Anselm passes without adequate justification from the *concept* of the most perfect Being to the assertion

[1] *Proslogion seu Alloquium de Dei existentia,* Ch. 2
[2] The name was given by Kant.

of His *existence,* and that the gap between conception and existence is a wide one; thus, we can conceive of a body having a velocity greater than 3.10^{10} centimeters per second, although no such velocity can exist anywhere in the universe. A further objection is that the phrase "a being than whom no more perfect being can be conceived," is suspiciously like the phrase "a number than which no greater number can be conceived," and the latter phrase does not correspond to anything that actually exists. However, one hesitates to condemn an argument which, though rejected by St. Thomas, has (in principle) been approved by Descartes, Newton, Leibnitz, and Hegel.

5
The beginnings of modern science

During the twelfth and thirteenth centuries there were many accessions to the list of classical texts known, at any rate in translations, to Western scholars. In the earlier Middle Ages there had been little of a philosophic or scientific kind available except the *Timaeus* of Plato (in a Latin version), and two of Aristotle's logical treatises (the *Categories* and the *De Interpretatione*), which had been translated by Boethius, together with Boethius' own writings on arithmetic, geometry, and music; and many leaders of thought, such as St. Gregory the Great, were not disposed to value such studies highly. About 1120 an English monk, Adelard of Bath, secured in Cordova an Arabic edition of the *Elements* of Euclid, and translated it into Latin. This work, and a translation of the *Algebra* of Al-Khowarizmi made in 1145 by Robert of Chester, were the real beginnings of modern exact science. Contact with the Mohammedan scholars, who had always followed the peripatetics rather than Plato, led to a knowledge of many works of Aristotle hitherto unknown in the West. In the latter half of the twelfth century and the early years of the thirteenth, many of his treatises (including the *Physics*) were introduced, having been translated from the original Greek into Syriac, from Syriac into Arabic, from Arabic into Hebrew, and finally from Hebrew into Latin. A little later the Greek text itself became available, and Latin translations were then made from the Greek directly.

6
Aristotle's physics

As it will be necessary frequently to refer to the physical and cosmological ideas of Aristotle, some account of them may be given at this point. The importance of Aristotle for our present inquiry depends on the fact that the medieval arguments for the existence of God were formulated at a time when Aristotelian ideas were dominant, and some consequences of this association still persist. The ordinary civilized man's outlook on the world, even today, includes elements derived ultimately from these ideas of Aristotle, which in some cases present difficulties in face of our modern science.

The leading idea throughout his treatment of nature was that of the *end* (τέλος). He applied this to inanimate objects by assuming that every body had an *essence* or specific nature (φύσις) which governed its behavior and impelled it to seek some place or condition; thus, earthly bodies tend to move downward, while fire-stuff moves upward. Motion was conceived as a means by which some essence could realize its inherent purpose; while the purpose was still unrealized, it was said to be in *potency* (δύναμις), and when realized, in *act,* (ἐνέργεια or ἐντέλεια), so that motion is the reduction of a condition of potency to a condition of act.

These concepts are far removed from the Newtonian idea of laws of motion which are the same for all kinds of matter; and there is another fundamental divergence between the Aristotelian and the modern outlook which must now be indicated. Modern natural philosophy is based on the hypothesis that there are a certain number of different kinds of elementary particles—electrons, protons, neutrons, positrons, etc.—and that the entire physical universe with all that happens in it is completely specified when we know the location and motions of these elementary particles—their aggregation into nuclei and atoms, the velocities of the atoms, etc. Aristotle on the other hand believed that it is not possible to explain all changes by motion in space; he regarded qualitative distinctions of substances as realities, and qualitative changes as essentially irreducible to variations in the location of elementary particles; indeed, he rejected completely the atomic theory of Democritus. These qualitative changes he subsumed under his principles of potency and act; between the original substance and the substance that results from the qualitative change, there is the relation of potency and act. Working out this idea, he postulated the existence of *prime matter* (πρώτη ὕλη), which was a general substrate having the potentiality of becoming a substance when it received a *form* (εἶδο), the form being the essential characteristic of the substance, that which makes it what it is; it was, so to speak, the soul of the thing. All natural bodies are thus resolved conceptually into matter and form; but the matter and form are only abstractions, the body alone having existence. Matter and form are related to each other as potency and act, the matter having the potentiality of becoming the recipient of form. "Matter" in Aristotle's sense is evidently not matter in our sense, and his "form" is not form in our sense; for example, a sculptured head has the figure but not the form (in Aristotle's sense) of a head, since it cannot perform the functions proper to a head.

7
The Aristotelian system of the world

Let us now pass to the consideration of Aristotle's system of the universe. Like all investigators of nature from Thales downward, he fastened on the distinction between things that are permanent and unalterable on the one hand, and things that are subject to generation and corruption on the other. Records of the old Babylonians and Egyptians showed that the stars had persisted without appreciable changes of position or brightness since the beginning of astronomical observation, whereas everything on earth was liable to alteration and decay. Aristotle therefore identified the perishable and imperishable parts of the cosmos with the earth and the heavenly bodies respectively. Thus he reached the conception of a universe composed of two unequal parts: a supralunar or celestial part, visible to us as the vault of the sky, and an infralunar or terrestrial part, consisting of the earth, which is a sphere, fixed and at rest in the center of the whole system. The celestial part has as its outermost constituent the "first heaven," which is a sphere carrying the fixed stars, and which has a movement of rotation directly brought about by God; the adhering stars are composed of an imperishable ether, and have no possibility of change or of any movement, save the uniform circular motion due to the rotating heaven; they are animated and intelligent beings, more divine than man. Terrestrial bodies were supposed by Aristotle to be compounded of the four elements of Empedocles, earth, air, water, and fire, each of which was supposed to have its own essential principle.

Within the first heaven, in this scheme, there are other rotating spheres carrying the planets, namely the five planets known to the ancients (Mercury, Venus, Mars, Jupiter, Saturn), together with the sun and moon. Each sphere rotates steadily, so that the only movements occurring in cosmology are uniform and circular; but in order to account for the apparently irregular wanderings of the planets, it was necessary to assume a complicated system of such circular motions, superposed on one another—*epicycles,* as they were called. This hypothesis had been proposed originally in the early part of the fourth century B.C. by Eudoxus, who had calculated that twenty-six uniform circular motions were needed. His method was in effect equivalent to analyzing the functions which represent the motions of the planets into sums of simply-periodic terms, as in fact is done in the modern mathematical treatment of the problem; from this point of view the spheres are merely descriptive of the periods, and have no bodily reality; but Aristotle, to whose mind mathematical abstractions were uncongenial, took the retrograde step of supposing that the spheres had corporeal existence, and further introduced divine beings to communicate to them their motions of rotation. He found himself obliged to postulate additional spheres in order to prevent the motion of any one sphere being communicated to all those inside it, and thus arrived finally at a total of forty-seven spheres.

Aristotle's physics and cosmology led him to a natural theology. The physics pointed to a Prime Mover[1] who is himself unmoved; in the cosmology the Prime Mover acts on the outermost of the spheres, whence by transmission all

[1] *Cf.* Book VIII of the *Physics*

the motions in the rest of the universe are derived; and this Prime Mover is Aristotle's God.[2] The Aristotelian natural theology had a powerful influence on St. Thomas, and indeed may have been the decisive factor in leading him to adopt the Aristotelian philosophy in general. Needless to say, St. Thomas was obliged to make considerable changes in Aristotle's God when adapting him to the service of Christian theism.

8
The Aristotelian treatment of causality

Any attempt to form a general conception of the universe, or to analyze the arguments for the existence of God, is bound to be affected profoundly by the view that is taken regarding the Principle of Causality. Indeed, we shall find it necessary to devote a considerable part of the present discussion to an account of the successive changes that have taken place in the idea of causation, changes that have been brought about largely by discoveries in the physical group of sciences.

What is a cause? The word belongs to common speech, and doubtless referred originally to the experience that we can by our own spontaneous activity bring about changes in the world; the changes are the "effect," our activity in producing them is the "cause." As Earl Russell says, "The conception of 'cause'—however loath we may be to admit

[2] *Cf.* Book V of the *Metaphysics*

the fact—is derived from the conception of 'will.'" The notion remained vague and unscientific until Aristotle took the matter in hand and gave his celebrated analysis of causality—his word for cause, αἰτία, being somewhat wider than the English word, and signifying everything that contributes to the production of an effect. He observed that for the constitution of a new object, four things are requisite, namely, something out of which it is made—this is the *Material Cause;* something to give it its specific nature—this is the *Formal Cause;* somebody or something to induce the formal cause in the material—this is the *Efficient Cause;* and a teleological principle or motive, on account of which the efficient cause acts—this is the *Final Cause.* Thus, in the production of a statue, the material cause would be the original block of marble, the formal cause would be the figure chiseled out, the efficient cause would be the sculptor, and the final cause would be the idea or likeness embodied in it. The Aristotelian doctrine of causality consists in a determination of the relations which these types of cause bear to one another, in the light of the physical knowledge of the time. It confirms the connection of the idea of "cause" with the idea of "will"; for, in Aristotle's cosmos, the efficient cause of the regular movements of the celestial spheres was affirmed to be intelligence, operating in a way analogous to human volition.

We must, however, be on our guard against supposing that the term *final cause* normally carries with it the notion of an agent whose intention was the constitution of the object; indeed, the idea of "final cause" in general approximates nearly to that of "function" or "purpose"; thus we may say that the final cause of the eye is sight, without necessarily implying the existence of a designer who formed the eye for the purpose of vision. This caution is needed in view of the argument from final causes which we shall presently meet with in Natural Theology, and which becomes confused and faulty unless the connotation of the words "final cause" is correctly understood.

9
The victory of Aristotle

Aristotle was received for many years with suspicion; by some critics, no doubt, from conservatism and the dislike of anything unfamiliar; by some, because of specific difficulties, such as that in the Aristotelian system the celestial spheres and their uniform rotations are eternal, and this seemed to be incompatible with the Christian doctrine of creation; and by some again, such as the Franciscan friar Roger Bacon, because they believed that the Aristotelian physics was completely wrong, and that the doctrine of matter and form, if it were accepted, would paralyze scientific research. In 1215 the Papal Legate actually prohibited the study of Aristotle's *Physics;* but the founding of the Orders of St. Francis and St. Dominic in the early years of the thirteenth century, and the rise of the universities, in which the friars became all-powerful, gave a new impetus to learning; the ascendancy of the Neoplatonic conceptions in Western Europe was gradually subverted, and in 1253 chairs of the Aristotelian philosophy were established in the University of Paris. A *Summa* of Aristotelian physics was written, probably about 1230, by Robert Greathead, then Rector of the Franciscans at Oxford; but the finally successful issue and culmination of the Aristotelian movement was in the work of the Dominicans St. Albert the Great and St. Thomas.

In view of the almost universal condemnation of Aristotelianism at the time of the Renaissance, it is of interest to inquire why its adoption in the thirteenth century may still rightly be acclaimed as a victory for progress. The general opinion has no doubt been formed by hostile interpretations: "Words, and more words, and nothing but words," wrote Macaulay in his essay on Francis Bacon, "the human mind, instead of marching, merely marked time." It has, however, been recognized by almost all subsequent theistic philosophers that from the point of view of their science, St. Thomas' reconstruction was a notable advance; for the transcendent (though non-ethical) God of Aristotle was better suited than the God of Plato for conversion into the God of Christianity. Moreover, the Aristotelian conception of the soul as the form of the body was better fitted than the Platonic conception of the body as the prison-house of the soul, to provide a philosophic interpretation of the Christian doctrine of resurrection. In the present discussion, however, the features to be stressed are, that Aristotle's influence encouraged the spirit of logic and of rational speculation, that he was much closer than Plotinus to Nature, and to empirical science, and that the result of his predominance was to obtain general acceptance for a conception of nature as a hierarchic order, with God as its ultimate foundation, and thus to establish the study of the external world as the foundation of natural theology. Philosophy, which in the earlier medieval writers had been dependent on Christian dogma, had henceforth an independent status, based on rational foundations; St. Albert the Great and St. Thomas were liberators who placed metaphysics and science securely within the domain of the free reason, who affirmed that no philosophy, not even their own, should be accepted on account of theological predilections.

It must not be forgotten that the attitude of Francis Bacon toward Aristotelianism had been to a great degree anticipated in the attitude of Aristotle himself toward the doctrines of his predecessors. In direct opposition to Plato, who held that the deceptions of sense justified skepticism of sense-information,[1] and who made intuition the ground of all true knowledge, Aristotle insisted in the strongest terms on experiment and observation as the sources of our understanding. "The principles which lie at the basis of any

---

[1] ἀπατης μεστὴ ἡ διὰ των ὀμμάτων σκέψις

[2] *Prior Analytics* I 30; *cf. De Coelo* I 10, II 13, III 8; *Met.* I 3, III 1

particular science," he wrote,[2] "are derived from experience (ἐμπειρία): thus it is from astronomical observation that we derive the principles of astronomical science." Essentially a naturalist, he poured scorn on ἀπειρία[3]—that is, the state of those who devote themselves entirely to abstract reasoning from intuitive postulates, and are indifferent to facts. "Those accustomed to physical inquiries are more competent," he asserted, "to lay down principles which have a wide application; whereas others who have been accustomed to many assumptions without the confrontation of reality, easily lay down principles because they take few things into consideration. It is easy to distinguish those who argue from facts and those who argue from notions." And he insisted on the importance of investigating every subject scientifically (φυσικως)—that is to say, by the study of sensible objects in nature[4]—rather than dialectically (λογικώς)—that is, by pure deduction from unproved assumptions. It is from sense that we gain the knowledge of particulars; from them by induction (ἐπαγωγή) we discover the universals in the particulars; and the only concern of science is with universals. "Let us first understand the facts, and then we may seek for the causes."[5]

---

[3] *De Gen. et Corr.* I 2
[4] *ibid.*
[5] *De Part.* I 1

10
The Five Ways

The principles thus asserted by Aristotle were adopted by St. Thomas,[1] and brought about in natural theology a radical change of orientation, which found expression in the famous *Five Ways* or Proofs of the existence of God.[2] As these will be frequently referred to in what follows, it may be well at this point to give a brief summary of them.

The First Proof, which seems to have been St. Thomas' favorite, since it is given much greater prominence than the others in the *Summa contra Gentiles*,[3] is called the *argument from motion,* and is essentially Aristotle's doctrine of the Prime Mover. The idea is that the changing world of nature is not a self-contained system. It should be explained that by the term *motion* he means change in general, and that he interprets it, as Aristotle had done, in terms of the Aristotelian concepts of potency and act. Now (the argument proceeds), nothing can be reduced from potency to act, except by something that is in a state of act; thus fire, which is actually hot, makes wood, which is potentially hot, to be actually hot. He then assumes that the same thing cannot be both in act and in potency at the same time and in the same respect; hence the thing initially in the state of act, which brings about the reduction, cannot be identical

1 *Cf.* St. Thomas, *Commentary on Aristotle's Physics* VIII 1

2 St. Thomas, *Summa Theol.* Ia, q. 2, art. 3

3 Book I, Ch. 13; *cf.* also *Compendium theologiae,* Part 1, sect. iii

with the thing initially in the state of potency, which undergoes the reduction—that is to say, a thing cannot be both mover and moved; whatever is moved must be moved by another—*omne quod movetur ab alio movetur.* All this is borrowed from Aristotle's *Physics;* the principle just stated is Aristotle's ἀνάγκη παν τὸ κινούμενον ὑπ' ἄλλου κινεισθαι.

St. Thomas then goes on to the second half of the proof, which consists in showing that if we pass from anything in motion to whatever it is that puts it in motion, and from the latter to its mover, and so on, then this process cannot go on to infinity: in his system, all earthly motions are dependent on the celestial motions—the propulsion of the heavenly spheres by angels; and it is necessary ultimately to postulate the existence of an unmoved mover, which must be of a different nature from the others. This first mover is God.

The Second Way, which is called the *proof from causality,* or the *etiological argument,* opens with the consideration that in the world of sense the connection between the present, the past, and the future is intelligible only on the principle of efficient causation; and a thing cannot be the efficient cause of itself; so everything has an efficient cause, which is distinct from itself: this again has its own cause, and so on; thus there is a sequence of efficient causes. This sequence cannot be infinite; it must lead up to an ultimate efficient cause which is itself uncaused: and this ultimate cause is God.

The idea of the Third Way, which is known as the *proof from contingent being,* or the *cosmological argument,*[4] may be traced back to Plato, but the form in which St. Thomas gives it is borrowed from the twelfth-century Jewish philosopher Maimonides.[5] It is based on the observation that everything in the world is contingent—that is, although it exists, its existence is not strictly necessary; we can think of it as not existing. Its existence therefore raises a problem: when we consider that there are two alternative possibilities, existence and non-existence, we see that there must be something that determines the matter one way or the other; so if it has existence, this must be from some cause. Thus, everything that is contingent has a cause. So, again rejecting the possibility of an infinite regress, we are led to assert the existence of a necessary being, existing of its own nature: and this necessary being is God.

The Fourth Way, which is known as the *argument from grades of perfection,* is reminiscent of the Stoics. "Chrysippus,"[6] says Balbus in Cicero's *Of the Nature of the Gods,*[7] "observes that everything in its kind, when it has arrived at maturity and perfection, is superior to that which has

---

[4] *Cf.* also the *Summa contra Gentiles* Book I, Ch. 15, and Book II, Ch. 15

[5] Maimonides (Rabbi Moses ben Maimon, 1135–1204), *Guide for the Perplexed* Part II, Ch. 1. Maimonides in turn borrowed the essentials of his argument from his Arab predecessor Avicenna (980-1037).

[6] B.C. 282–209, the third of the founders of the Stoic philosophy, his predecessors being Zeno and Cleanthes

[7] II 14

not; as a horse to a colt, a dog to a puppy, and a man to a boy; so whatever is best must exist in some perfect and consummate being." St. Thomas' argument runs thus: Among existing things there are some more and less good, true, noble, etc. But the words "more" and "less" presuppose the existence of a standard which embodies the quality concerned in the highest degree, so that there is something which is best, something truest, something noblest, and so on; the existence of the good implies the existence of something supremely and absolutely good, which is its pattern: and this pattern is God.

The Fifth Way is known as the *proof from order,* or *from the government of things.*[8] St. Thomas ascribes it[9] to St. John Damascene, but, as we have seen (§ 2), it occurs very frequently in the writings of both Jews and Stoics. In Greek thought it can be traced back to the pre-Socratic philosophers and to Socrates himself, and it is prominent in the *Timaeus* of Plato. Cicero presents it most impressively, taking as the basis of his argument the motions of the heavenly bodies.[10] In one form or another, it is found over and over again in the Fathers.

In order to describe the argument as presented by St. Thomas, we must first refer to the doctrine promulgated in the fifth century before Christ by the Greek atomists,

[8] Often as the *teleological argument;* but for reasons given later, I do not regard this name as appropriate.

[9] *Summa contra Gentiles* I 13

[10] *De Natura Deorum* II 34, 35

Leucippus and Democritus, who taught that all the phenomena of the universe are produced by innumerable small particles, eternal and unchangeable, which move about in empty space, frequently colliding, and associating with one another in various combinations. The world so pictured was entirely atheistic and materialistic, and there was no design behind it.

St. Thomas starts from a denial of the atomist teaching, asserting as the premise of his reasoning that natural bodies in the world are in fact disposed in harmonious order, and operate in such a way as to subserve good or desirable ends; in short, he attaches himself to the Aristotelian doctrine of Final Causes, in the sense of functions or intrinsic purposes. But, he says, things which are not endowed with the faculty of intelligence or reason do not tend toward a definite purpose unless they are directed by some intelligent being, as for instance an arrow by an archer; hence they must be governed not by chance but by intention. Therefore, there exists some intelligent being by which all natural things are ordered to a providential design: and this is the being we call God.

The Five Ways evidently supplement one another by presenting God in different aspects. Thus the conception of Him derived from the Fifth Proof taken alone is not incompatible with pantheism, and in any case presents God only as the architect of the cosmos; it needs to be enriched by the conclusions of the Third Proof, that He is self-existent and necessary, and of the Fourth Proof, that He is the perfect pattern.

11
Different kinds of proof

It may be proper at this point to make some comments on the proofs as a whole. A proof has been defined as a process by which A induces in B a sense of the justification for a conviction. The highest type of proof is the kind that is found in pure mathematics, such as the proof of Lagrange's theorem that any number can be expressed as the sum of four squares, or of Gauss's theorem that any prime number of the form $(4n + 1)$ can be expressed as the sum of two squares. These proofs depend on no premises whatever, except purely logical propositions, which are universally accepted as the necessary presuppositions of reasoning: they constitute, therefore, inescapable demonstrations which have a coercive power over the minds of all sane persons. It is evident that proofs of the existence of God cannot belong to this class. For if a coercive proof could be devised, it would doubtless have been discovered before now, and would have convinced all those able philosophers among our contemporaries who do not in fact accept any of the proofs hitherto put forward.

The proofs of assertions regarding the results of scientific experiments, such as the statement that water is composed of hydrogen and oxygen, are of an entirely different character from those of pure mathematics. The proof of the former class involves an excursion into the external world, and depends essentially on the principle that experiments such as those of compounding and dissociating water can be repeated as often as we like at different locations in space and different instants of time, and that in the past they have always given the same results; whence, on the ground of a belief in the regularity of Nature, we conclude that the result happens invariably. Evidently no proofs of the existence of God can be quite of this type.

The processes by which a schoolmaster induces in his pupils the belief that Julius Caesar invaded Britain in B.C. 55 are obviously of a different character again, the credibility of testimony now being prominent. Although theological statements may be established by arguments which involve the credibility of testimony, such arguments belong to the domain of revealed rather than of natural religion, and so are of no relevance for our present purpose.

12
Preliminary comments on the Five Ways

St. Thomas' proofs of the existence of God cannot be referred to any of the types we have mentioned. Their most obvious characteristic is that the starting-point from which they proceed lies in experience; they take for granted the existence of the external world, and are grounded in Nature. To this indeed was chiefly due their great importance for the history of religion. The Five Ways are not of Christian origin: they are all to be found substantially in Plato, or Aristotle, or the Stoics, or Maimonides; and St. Thomas, in reproducing the arguments of his pagan and Jewish predecessors, made little or no change in them. But his rejection of St. Anselm's ontological proof in favor of the Five Ways marked a great and wholesome revolution in the Christian outlook, a new orientation toward the external material world, a recognition of the creation as the primary evidence of the Creator. The long night of Neoplatonism was now ended, and the contempt of matter was a thing of the past.

The arguments depend fundamentally on the recognition of connections between events, which make it possible to arrange them in chains or sequences, each sequence leading up to, and terminating in, God. In the formation of the sequences, the principle of causality plays a ruling part. St. Thomas' thought is dominated by the Aristotelian idea that behind all phenomena there are *causes* which are knowable entities. Nature is conceived as held together by chains of causations which are suspended, so to speak, from the divinity. The concept of "cause" has been greatly modified since Aristotle's time, and his notion of it has been replaced in modern physics by the concepts of mathematical law and predictability; the repercussions of this changed situation on natural theology will be postponed for the present, and taken up later.

Next, we notice that the last step in each proof depends on *analogy,* the principle that when two different things show parallelism in some respects, we may be justified in attributing to one of them something which we know definitely of the other, and which is associated with the respects in which there is parallelism. Analogy is of fundamental importance in the system of St. Thomas. Thus in the Fifth Proof, the order and harmony of the universe are adduced as showing that Nature is tending toward the fulfilment of a purpose; and this is so exactly parallel to the tendency of material bodies to seek their proper place that we are led by analogy to ascribe to nature a similar to the [illegible] φύσις of material bodies.

Analogy, like induction, is essentially an inference from sampling, and has the incompleteness that affects all inferences from sampling: there can be no absolute certainty in an argument which infers the existence of unknown entities from the mere fact of the existence of certain other entities. In practical life, however, an inference from sampling can very often indeed be a reasonable ground for one's belief and action.

It is evident that principles such as those of causality and analogy carry us beyond direct observation and experiment, and belong rather to the ontological and transcendental domain—to metaphysics, in fact; and this explains why the proofs have no coercive character; it is because there is no general agreement on questions of metaphysics.

Another general remark that may find a place at this stage is that proofs must be relative to our culture and conditioned by it. This remark applies even to the proofs of theorems in pure mathematics, which, as we saw, depend on the fewest assumptions; for even those assumptions, namely the fundamental principles of logic, are liable to change. In recent years they have been challenged in an important respect by the work of Brouwer, of which some mention may be made here. At the basis of the traditional logic there is the "Principle of the Excluded Middle," which asserts that either a proposition or its negation is true. Brouwer subjects the word "true" to a critical examination, and decides that unless there is some imaginable means of ascertaining whether a proposition is true or not, the concept of its truth serves no useful purpose, and therefore that the only connotation of the word "true" which deserves to be retained is that of "verifiable." Correspondingly, a proposition is not to be called "false" unless its negation is a verifiable proposition. Take an example in mathematics, namely the expression of π (the ratio of the circumference of a circle to its diameter) as a number; it is 3.1415926536 . . . , where the decimal does not terminate, although we can calculate it to as many places as we choose. Now consider the proposition that "somewhere in this decimal there is a sequence of ten digits 5 occurring in succession, thus: 5555555555." It is of course conceivable that we might come upon such a sequence by actual calculation of the decimal, in which case the proposition would be true; or we might conceivably construct a general proof that such a sequence could not exist, in which case the proposition would be false; but clearly these are not the only alternatives: the proposition is not necessarily either verifiable or the negation of a verifiable proposition—that is, it is not necessarily either true or false, in the sense in which these words are now to be used. The stark antithesis of the old "true" and "false" does not adequately represent the possibilities that should be recognized and distinguished in the logic of propositions. For such a proposition, therefore, the "Principle of the Excluded Middle" should not be postulated; and, as Brouwer and his disciples have shown, a satisfactory system of logic can be constructed in which it is not assumed. This "three-valued logic," as it is called, has recently been shown to be of the greatest value in resolving the paradoxes of quantum-mechanics. What seems to one generation to be an unquestionable intuitive basic principle of logic does not seem to have this character in the opinion of a later generation, which has a wider outlook on what is actually possible in the cosmos.

At this point we may say a word regarding the objections which have been brought against the Proofs by medieval and modern writers, reserving the discussion of them until later. Some of them do little more than demonstrate the non-coercive character of the arguments, without sensibly diminishing their effective appeal; and indeed much of the criticism that has been directed at them by professional philosophers has, I venture to think, misapprehended the nature of their claim to consideration and the object for which they were devised. St. Thomas was not an abstract metaphysician spinning cobwebs *in vacuo,* but a Christian priest, whose aim was one of practical apologetics: he set out not to provide demonstrations of the same coercive quality as those of mathematical theorems regarding numbers, but to present arguments of such a character that a man would be reasonably justified in acting on them. Some metaphysical assumptions are made, regarding which it is possible for thoughtful men to hold contradictory opinions; but the ordinary man makes these assumptions with his eyes open, and is usually willing to make them. My own aim is likewise practical. I leave on one side many abstract philosophical questions, and concentrate rather on a humbler, but I hope useful, inquiry as to whether the conceptions of the external world on which St. Thomas based his arguments have been affected by the development of scientific knowledge since the thirteenth century.

Some of the objections which relate to specific elements in the reasoning of particular Proofs may be briefly mentioned here in anticipation of a more complete discussion later.

The first proof, or the proof from motion, is open to the objection, first brought against it by Duns Scotus and William of Ockham, that the principle *omne quod movetur ab alio movetur,* on which the whole argument depends, is irreconcilable with sound dynamical science, and is therefore false.

The second argument, that from chains of cause and effect, must take account of the altered views of causality that have followed first from Newtonianism, and then from quantum theory, and must justify itself against Kant's objection, that the principle of causality is applicable only within the world of experience.

Against the Third Way, which rests on the ideas of contingency and necessity, Kant objected that contingency and necessity are merely categories set up by the human mind, which need not correspond to anything objective; and that St. Thomas' argument really involves a dependence on the ideas of St. Anselm's ontological proof, which Kant and St. Thomas agree in rejecting. Moreover, Professor Broad objects [1] that there are no "necessary beings," because "necessity" is a modal predicate that applies to propositions only, and never to things or to what is existent.

Against the Fourth Way, the proof from degrees of perfection, the criticism has been made that the same argument, when applied in a different context, can lead to less acceptable conclusions; in short, that it lends itself too easily to burlesque. For instance, it will be admitted that some people have a stronger sense of humor than others; but (following the argument of the Fourth Proof) this presupposes the existence of a standard which embodies the

[1] *Theism and Cosmology* (London, 1940), p. 98

possession of a sense of humor in the highest degree, which is, so to speak, supremely humorous and the pattern of all humor; and still following the argument of the Fourth Proof, we should apparently be led to the conclusion that this pattern is God. The defense against criticism of this kind is, no doubt, to point out that there is implicit in St. Thomas' argument the idea of moral value. Now moral value is of course very real and important, and is the basis of some excellent arguments for the existence of God: but it carries us beyond the consideration of the external material world; the Fourth Way thus belongs to a somewhat different domain of thought from the other Ways, and I shall regard it as outside the scope of the present work.

The Fifth Way, that from order, or the government of things, has been in some form the favorite of most modern Christian apologists. But its reputation has suffered from injudicious and careless presentations: it has sometimes been expressed in the form "The existence of design proves the existence of a designer," which is evidently nothing more than a mere tautology. However, partly as a result of the criticisms of Hume in his *Dialogues concerning Natural Religion* (published in 1779), and Kant in his *Critique of Pure Reason* (published in 1781), the argument was clarified and improved by the writers who came after them; the modern outlook on the cosmos is discussed in § 40.

To sum up, we may say that with St. Thomas' Five Ways there are entwined more or less closely certain doctrines regarding motion, causality, cosmology, and teleology, which were derived from Aristotelian sources. Our purpose is to inquire how far those doctrines, or the dependence of the arguments on them, have been illumined or affected by the later developments of natural philosophy.

13
The Franciscan school

Side by side with Thomism there flourished a somewhat different type of medieval philosophy, which is of great interest from the fact that it was the direct ancestral form of modern science. Its principal representatives were connected with the Franciscan Order: from the point of view of our present subject, their most important distinguishing quality was that they avoided, in a greater or less degree, the erroneous Aristotelian physics and cosmology.

The sequence begins with Robert Greathead, or Robert of Lincoln (1175–1253), the first Rector of the Franciscans at Oxford (though not actually himself a member of the Order), afterwards Bishop of Lincoln. Greathead maintained the Pythagorean doctrine that the key to the interpretation of the external world is to be found in its structure, which can be expressed in mathematical language—that is, by means of numbers: numerical law, analogous to the laws of harmony in music, was to be discerned in all phenomena. His own interest had been formed chiefly by the optical writings of the Arab astronomer ibn-al-Haytham (Alhazen), who flourished in the latter part of the tenth and early part of the eleventh century; and he devoted most attention to the laws of perspective and to a cosmology of his own, which was based on the idea of light as the primary substance.

His pupil, Roger Bacon, whose long life extended from the second to the last decade of the thirteenth century, was a Franciscan friar. Bacon was not only a mathematician and astronomer (he was the first to estimate with tolerable accuracy the error of the Julian calendar), but also a practical research worker in physics, who studied the properties of lenses, and invented spectacles for certain defects of vision. In chemistry he performed a great many experiments, though he did not succeed in devising new general theories to replace the erroneous ideas of his day. His importance in the history of thought rests on his clear perception that physical questions could not be solved by the methods of his contemporaries, *rationaliter,* that the search for the Aristotelian Forms and Species was idle folly; and that the true *prima philosophia* should be constituted of all the fixed and universal laws of nature. Observational science, in Roger Bacon's view, is the presupposition of metaphysical philosophy, which is obtained from it by a process of distillation, so to speak, the relation of metaphysics to science being like the relation of the attar of roses to the flowers from which it is produced.

14
Ockham's criticism of the First Way

These principles were developed later by another Franciscan friar, who became known as the ablest philosopher of the fourteenth century, William of Ockham. With Ockham's purely metaphysical doctrines we are not here directly concerned; but his work was of the highest importance, both for natural philosophy and for natural theology. Though not professing any scorn of Aristotle, he came into violent collision with the Aristotelians when he rejected the principle, "Whatever is in motion is put in motion by another." Ockham's argument, which was based on considerations amounting virtually to the discovery of the law of inertia, will perhaps be made more clear, without being altered in essence, if the law of inertia is enunciated in the later form, namely, that *every body continues in its state of rest or of uniform motion in a straight line, except in so far as it may be compelled by force to change that state.* Consider a star [1] which has never been near enough to another star to be appreciably influenced by it, and which therefore has always moved, and is still moving, in a straight line through interstellar space. This star is continually changing its location, and is therefore "moved"; but the whole point of the law of inertia is that in motion of this type there is no "mover." The star has never been subjected to any influence whatever,

[1] The introduction of stellar motions is, of course, placing Ockham's argument in a modern setting.

and yet its position is continually changing; it is "moved." Ockham therefore concluded that the maxim, "Whatever is in motion must be put in motion by another," is false.

The Aristotelian rejoinder to this objection involves some of the technicalities of their philosophy, and, as it may not interest the general reader, is relegated to an appendix (p. 133). Suffice it here to say, that their argument does not succeed in reconciling the maxim with modern dynamics.

The well-known aphorism known as "Ockham's razor," that "entities must not be multiplied unnecessarily," though not actually to be found in Ockham's works, correctly represents his doctrine. In the Aristotelian scheme, whenever a phenomenon was discussed, an entity was invented to account for it—*oportet ponere aliquod agens.* In the light of the new principle, Ockham denied that different kinds of matter were required for the constitution of terrestrial and celestial bodies—an anticipation which was not fully verified until the time of Tycho Brahé, more than two centuries later.

15
The Ockhamist school at Paris

Ockham's refutation of the Aristotelian doctrine of motion greatly strengthened the tradition which had been founded by Robert Greathead and Roger Bacon; and in the University of Paris, where Ockham's influence was predominant, the conviction became general that philosophers had been wasting their time in analyzing, subdividing, and classifying the ideas of their own minds, and in constructing syllogisms about entities and quiddities. The true interpretation of the world, it was now realized, could be discovered only by the patient study of Nature.

One of the leaders of the Parisian school, Nicolas of Autrecourt, proposed to abandon the Aristotelian representation of change as the succession of different forms in the same subject, and to introduce in its place the fundamental hypothesis of modern physics, that all change in the material universe can be accounted for by the interaction and motion of elementary particles. This was in some sense a return to the doctrine of the Greek atomists, which Aristotle had rejected; but it is to be remembered that in the theory as formulated by Democritus and Epicurus, the atoms were supposed to be incapable of acting on each other except by actual contact, whereas the more modern representation was free of this restriction, and so left open the possibility of explaining "fields" such as that of gravitation. Another member of the same group, a pupil of Ockham's, was a secular priest named Jean Buridan, who became Rector of the University of Paris in 1327. Continuing Ockham's work on the motion of bodies, Buridan arrived at the notion of *impetus* or *momentum* almost as it was conceived three centuries later by Galileo, Descartes, and Newton.

The greatest name of the Parisian school, however, was that of Nicole Oresme, Bishop of Lisieux from 1377 to

1382. In a commentary on the *De Coelo* of Aristotle, written in 1377, he argued in favor of attributing the apparent diurnal motion of the stars to the earth and not to the heavens, thus anticipating Copernicus; and he investigated successfully the motion of a body which moves in a straight line with uniform acceleration, showing that the space described in any interval of time is the same as if it had no acceleration, but a uniform velocity equal to the velocity which it had at the mid-instant of the interval of time.

16
Why the new Platonism was an advance

Under the pressure of the vigorous current of new ideas proceeding from the Ockhamists, the Aristotelian tradition, in Paris at any rate, decayed; and at any time after the middle of the fourteenth century there was a considerable body of opinion which regarded Aristotelianism as mere sterile pedantry, having no relation to truth or reality: as Erasmus said later, "looking in utter darkness for that which has no existence whatever." After the death of Oresme, however, the vitality not only of the Aristotelians but also of the Parisian school of natural philosophy became exhausted, and the study of Nature languished until it was awakened by the rise of a new movement in the fifteenth century. This was neither more nor less than a revival of Platonism.

That such a revival should tend to the encouragement of natural science may seem surprising. If the supersedure of

Plato by Aristotle was such a great step forward in the thirteenth century, why should a reversal of the process be likewise a great step forward two centuries later?

The explanation is, that the Platonism of the Renaissance was something totally different from the Neoplatonism which had prevailed before the thirteenth century. As we have seen, the old Neoplatonism held material things in profound contempt; the new Platonism on the other hand had an exuberant joy in Nature and a passionate interest in the Arts and in Science. Thus the two parties in the controversy between Platonists and Aristotelians really changed sides as between the thirteenth century and the fifteenth: on the former occasion it was the Aristotelians who claimed for the external world its rightful consideration in philosophy, and particularly in natural theology; in the later struggle it was the Platonists who were the party of progress, who aimed at freeing natural philosophy from bondage to traditionalism, and who stressed the importance of experimental science. The introduction of Aristotle by St. Albert the Great and St. Thomas had brought life and liberty; the attempt to retain him in the sixteenth and seventeenth centuries would, if it had been successful, have brought intellectual death.

There is, however, still something to be explained. Why did the philosophers of the fifteenth century, in their disgust with Aristotle, revert to Plato? The answer may partly be that, in rejecting the Aristotelian conception of objects as compounded of form and matter, they found it natural to go back to Plato's original conception of the Forms as eternal Ideas. But another, and perhaps stronger reason, was a new attitude toward mathematics. Platonists and Neoplatonists had always been interested in that subject; whether the inscription ἀγεωμέτρητος μηδεὶς εἰσίτω [1] ever adorned the Academy or not, the mathematical (and particularly the numerical) interest of, for example, the *Timaeus* is unmistakable: and the last great teacher of the school, Proclus, was also the last eminent mathematician of the ancient world. However, the disdain of Nature, which was characteristic of Neoplatonist philosophy, disjoined mathematics in the earlier Middle Ages from experimental science, and caused numerical work to be ignored in favor of logical developments. This is, I believe, the true explanation of the historical fact that mathematics made practically no progress for nearly a thousand years. Early in the twelfth century, as we have seen, the *Elements* of Euclid were translated into Latin and became known to Western scholars; but the conception of natural philosophy derived from this source fitted in only too well with the prevailing alienation from experiment. By Euclid, the science of geometry was presented as a chain of propositions obtained by syllogistic reasoning from a small number of original premises. From whence were these premises derived? Plato believed that they could all be obtained by pure intellection; and Euclid drew up a list of five "common notions" or axioms and five "postulates," from which he professed to demonstrate

[1] "Let no one destitute of geometry enter."

all the results of geometry as logical conclusions. Neither for common notions nor for postulates was any proof offered; the disciple was expected to know by intuition that they were necessary, that things could not be otherwise. Thus the Greek philosophers taught that although geometry was a science relating to the sensible universe, it could be built up completely without having recourse at any stage to quantitative observation.

In spite of the explicit declarations of Aristotle and St. Thomas that the only secure foundation is experiment, the schoolmen generally followed the lead of Euclid, and held that results of value relating to the external world could be obtained by syllogistic reasoning based on self-evident premises. Their interest was concentrated on pure deduction; and this was not uncongenial to their general outlook; for, recognizing in the physical order an expression of the Divine Reason, they inferred that the human reason was the proper organ for its investigation. This excessively logical conception of science proved to be harmful, and the sterility of the Aristotelian philosophy as regards scientific research became too evident to be ignored. At this stage the new spirit of the Renaissance, with its fervent delight in the world of matter, responded eagerly to the suggestion that genuine science must be quantitative, and that human understanding of the sensible universe must be expressible in terms of numerical relations. Resurgent Platonism proclaimed that the book of Nature is written by God, in the language of mathematics.

17
Copernicus

The modern history of theories of the universe begins with the publication in 1543 of the treatise of Copernicus *De Revolutionibus orbium coelestium.* From this work as a beginning there has developed in the course of four centuries an understanding of the cosmos, which now forms the most sublime and wonderful chapter in the book of man's knowledge of Nature.

Nicolaus Copernicus was born in a town on the Vistula in 1473. Losing his father at an early age, he came under the guardianship of his mother's brother, the bishop of a neighboring diocese, who sent him at the age of eighteen to the University of Cracow. On completing his course there he proceeded to Italy, and, after studying canon law, philosophy, medicine, and astronomy at Padua and Bologna, returned to Cracow and entered the Church; shortly afterward he was appointed a canon of the Cathedral of the Assumption at Frauenburg, where the rest of his life was spent.

Like Newton, Copernicus seems to have disliked publishing his discoveries; on this account it is impossible to say precisely when the most celebrated of them was made, but about 1531 he circulated a manuscript indicating it briefly, and in 1533 a certain Albert Widmanstad explained the new system to Pope Clement VII. The *De Revolutionibus* was, however, written only at the very end of his life.

What was Copernicus' great contribution to science? The usual statement is, that before his time the sun was believed to revolve round the earth, whereas he taught that the earth revolved round the sun; that the question was, in short, whether it is the earth or the sun that is at rest in space.

What has modern science to say on this question? The notions of "rest" and "motion" have been analyzed carefully in the present century by the creators of the theory of relativity, who have shown that there is no such thing as absolute "rest." When we say that a thing is "at rest," we mean that it has no motion relative to some standard body which is taken to be "at rest"; in ordinary life we say that anything is at rest if it is immobile relative to the earth's surface, which implies that we are taking the earth's surface as the standard body. But unless some standard body of reference is presupposed, there is no meaning in the phrase "at rest"; to talk of a body being "at rest in space" is simply nonsense.

Thus we seem to be led to the paradoxical conclusion that the Copernican doctrine, which has often been called—and justly called—the greatest revolution that has ever taken place in human thought, consisted in substituting for the meaningless statement "the earth is at rest in space," the statement "the sun is at rest in space," which is equally meaningless.

But this is not the only puzzling circumstance connected with Copernicanism. As we have seen, it had been explained to Pope Clement VII, who appears to have been not unfavorably impressed; and when the *De Revolutionibus* was published, it was dedicated to Pope Paul III and was prefaced by a letter of commendation from Cardinal Nicholas Schönberg, Archbishop of Padua. The work of a canon, praised by a cardinal and benevolently regarded by two Popes, it seems to have encountered no opposition in high ecclesiastical circles at the time or for more than one generation afterward. It was, indeed, not until 1616—seventy-three years after the death of Copernicus—that the affair of Galileo began, and the Congregation of the Index found his teaching in certain respects objectionable. During these seventy-three years the Copernican theory had been steadily making headway, had inspired many discoveries of the first importance in astronomy, and had become the generally received opinion of men of science. One feels that there is something to be explained in this story: if there was any question about Copernicanism being contrary to received doctrines in philosophy or theology, how did it happen that the matter was not raised earlier? Why was no objection taken until the new hypothesis had the prestige of seventy-three successful years behind it?

I shall try to give the solution of the two problems that have been indicated; it will appear that they are intimately connected, so that the solution of one will lead naturally to the solution of the other.

The explanation depends on the fact, which is of capital importance throughout natural philosophy, that a correct *mathematical* solution of a phenomenon (that is to say, a set of mathematical formulae which enable us to predict the occurrence and course of the phenomenon) does not necessarily furnish the correct *physical* description of the phenomenon (that is to say, the specification of the actual physical mechanism by which the phenomenon is produced). For instance in the case of the planetary motions, the mathematical formulae obtained by postulating Aristotle's 47 celestial spheres gave (within the degree of accuracy expected in the Middle Ages) correct values for the places of the planets in the sky; but this did not prove that the 47 spheres had physical existence. Or, to take another example, the theory that light consists of waves in an elastic-solid ether provides mathematical formulae which account perfectly for all the phenomena of interference and diffraction in optics; and yet no one now believes that such an ether exists.

The Greeks were well aware of this distinction, and used the expression σώζειν τὰ φαινόμενα, "to save appearances"—in scholastic terminology, *salvare apparentias*—whenever a mathematical formula was obtained which described the observed facts and made prediction possible; such a formula did not necessarily provide an explanation κατὰ φύσιν, "conformable to the nature of things"—that is to say, an explanation of a deeper or more physical kind, dealing with real existence, *in esse et secundum rem,* as the scholastics expressed it.

The amount of opposition which a new doctrine like that of Copernicus might be expected to evoke depended very much on whether it offered itself merely as an improved way of "saving appearances," or whether it claimed to provide a new understanding of the nature of things. In the former case, as a purely "formalist" theory, it would be merely an affair of the mathematicians, and nobody would wish to hinder them from doing their calculations in whatever way they preferred; but in the latter case, that is, when put forward as a "realist" explanation, it might conflict with beliefs generally held by cosmologists, philosophers, and even theologians, and might give rise to heated controversy.

It was open to Copernicus to choose either alternative. He might adopt the formalist position, stressing the advantages that would be gained in astronomical calculations and in the simplicity of cosmological description by taking the sun as the origin of co-ordinates (to use a mathematical term which became current after his day), without affirming that this necessarily entailed any conclusions about physical reality; or he might come forward as a realist, presenting his theory as a new doctrine in natural philosophy, namely, that the sun, and not the earth, is at rest in space. In the one case, he would be introducing a policy, and in the other a creed. Actually, the decision was taken out of his hands; for Andreas Osiander, the friend to whom he entrusted the publication of the *De Revolutionibus,* composed and inserted a preface, which, being unsigned, was for long believed to be the work of Copernicus himself; and in this preface Osiander took up the formalist position quite definitely; thereby securing the result at which he aimed, of disarming any attacks which might otherwise have been made by the Aristotelian philosophers. A long period was thus gained during which the Copernican ideas could be developed in comparative peace.

18

The decadence of scholasticism

As we have already seen, in the latter part of the fourteenth century the followers of William of Ockham made important discoveries in physical science. After the Renaissance the inheritors of the Ockhamist tradition, being in full sympathy with the mathematical and experimental method, tended to merge themselves in the general body of those who cultivated it, and to lose their vitality as a separate school of metaphysicians, thus leaving the Aristotelians as the sole professed continuators of medieval philosophy. Moreover the Aristotelians recovered some of their lost prestige, as a result of the work of writers such as the Italian Dominican Cardinal Cajetan (1469–1534), and in the following century the Spanish Jesuit Francisco Suarez (1548-1617). But the Aristotelians never accepted the principle that the structure of the inanimate world is essentially mathematical; it was this principle, derived from Plato and ultimately from the Pythagoreans, that was to inspire the men of the new age, and it was the failure of the later scholastics to assimilate it that led, more than any other single circumstance, to the alienation of men of science from medieval philosophy. Moreover, scholasticism was decadent in that the love of Nature that had been so vital in Aristotle had almost perished: the practice of observation and experiment, on which he and St. Thomas had so strongly insisted, was neglected; and the degenerate schoolmen occupied themselves with futile subtleties that bore no relation to life and reality: they argued about homogeneities and heterogeneities, categorematices and syncategorematices, simpliciters, and secundum quids; they resolved questions by the way of formaliter, materialiter, fundamentaliter, and eminenter; and showed the causes of things in sympathy, antipathy, and the influence of the heavens. No wonder that the virile scholars of the Renaissance broke away from it all. In Italy, under the patronage of the Medici, the revived Platonism was dominant; and at Paris in 1536, a crowded audience acclaimed the thesis of Peter Ramus, "Whatever is in Aristotle is false."

19
Tycho and Kepler

If philosophy and science were to be restored to life and health, the first necessity, as Ramus saw, was to return to the path that had been opened up by the Ockhamists of the fourteenth century, and to re-establish contact with the external world. The pioneer in the new movement back to Nature was a friend of Ramus, the Danish astronomer Tycho Brahé, who lived from 1546 to 1601, and was thus about twenty years senior to Francis Bacon and Galileo, and a century earlier than Newton. His observations though made before the invention of the telescope and the micrometer, were astonishingly accurate, and some of his deductions from them were soon seen to be incompatible with the Aristotelian system of the world; thus his memoir on a new star which appeared in the constellation Cassiopeia in 1572, by showing that this object was situated among the fixed stars, destroyed the belief in the incorruptibility of the heavenly bodies, which was at the time regarded as an integral part of scholastic philosophy; and his proof that the comet of 1577 moved round the sun in planetary space, shattered the cosmology which located comets in the earth's atmosphere.

The work of Tycho firmly established the principle that natural philosophy must be based on quantitative data acquired from observation. But something more was needed in order to consummate the foundation of modern science, and this further element was contributed by his pupil Kepler. Kepler's idea, which he derived from the revived Platonism then in favor, was traceable ultimately to the Pythagoreans. The original Pythagorean discovery related to the lengths of the strings of a lyre: it was found that if a string is stopped at half its length it gives a note one octave higher; if at two-thirds its length, it gives a note higher by the musical interval called a fifth, and so on. Thus simple numerical ratios were shown to exist between the lengths of strings which produce sounds harmonious to one another, and so a connection was set up between mathematics and aesthetics. This was generalized into the principle that numerical laws, analogous to the numerical laws of harmony in music, were the proper means of interpreting the fundamental unity of the cosmos; that there must be a mathematical harmony of the external world, underlying all phenomena; that this was the reality which philosophers sought, and that the task of men of science was to find it.

Moreover, it was asserted that the dispositions of Nature were of the simplest character that could be imagined in any particular case. This consideration, which has in fact played a part of the first importance in the history of physics—in our day it guided Einstein to the law of gravitation in curved space—was applied by Kepler in order to simplify the elaborate picture of the world which he had inherited from his predecessors. It is to be remembered that Copernicus, although he took the all-important step of placing the sun in the center of the universe, still retained the intricate machinery of epicycles which had been devised by Eudoxus and Hipparchus to represent the motions of the planets, and which by the successive adjunction of fresh curves to represent new discoveries, had by now become intolerably complicated; so much so that a royal patron of science, to whom it was described, remarked that "if the Deity had consulted him at the creation, he would have given Him good advice." It seemed to Kepler that the truth must be much simpler than anyone had yet realized, and that by use of the right kind of mathematics, it should be possible to exhibit or suggest in some way a physical connection between the planets and the sun as the center of their motions. In 1604 he found that when the sun was taken as origin of co-ordinates, the path of the planet Mars was an ellipse; this was an immense improvement in simplicity over the complicated system of epicycles that had been used in the older astronomy. Later he found that the orbits of Mercury, Venus, Jupiter, and Saturn were also ellipses, whose planes passed through the sun, and which were described according to a very simple rule. These laws were announced in 1609. The earth was found to obey exactly the same laws of motion relative to the sun as the other planets; and thus the mathematical theory led to the conviction that the earth simply *was* a planet, and that Aristotle's distinction between the incorruptible heavenly bodies and terrestrial corruption was false.

20
Galileo and the later Aristotelians

The conclusions arrived at by Tycho and Kepler, by which the true structure of the solar system was revealed, thoroughly alarmed the Aristotelians. They now saw that Copernicanism, even if promulgated originally as no more than a mathematical theory, had in fact led to consequences irreconcilable with their cosmology; and they resolved to take action. The appearance in 1613 of Galileo's *Letters on the Solar Spots* gave them an opportunity to attack the most eminent living advocate of the Copernican ideas; and in 1616 the storm broke.

In order to appreciate the true significance of the Galileo controversy, it is necessary to distinguish between the real and the nominal issue. The real issue was whether it was possible any longer to maintain the Aristotelian distinction in kind between the earth and the heavenly bodies—the one as the abode of generation and decay, the other as unchanging and eternal. The breaking down of this distinction was the great work achieved by the Copernican revolution: once it was done, the way was cleared for the discovery of laws of Nature, such as the Newtonian laws of motion and of gravitation, *operating over the entire universe.* But Galileo's opponents cleverly evaded the broad question—on which the observational evidence against them had by now become conclusive—and managed to keep the legal process focused on the much narrower issue of whether Copernicanism should be interpreted in the "realist" or in the "formalist" sense, with Galileo as the champion of realism. Looking back, we can see that Galileo was unwise in allowing himself to be maneuvered into this position: he would have been better advised to make his stand on a more favorable battleground; for the realist interpretation of Copernicanism—the doctrine that the sun is at rest in space—was, in the nature of things, incapable of proof, and has in fact been discarded by modern science. In 1633 the victory at law went to the Aristotelians; but to stifle the discoveries of the preceding half century was now impossible, and the legal decision won availed them nothing.

The imbecility of their champions in the seventeenth century was almost beyond belief. They followed up the condemnation of Galileo by an attack on experimental science in general, producing the most amazing arguments for discrediting their opponents. One of them asked why we cannot see better with two pairs of spectacles than with one singly, since *Vis unita fortior;* and inferred that results obtained by placing one lens in front of another, as in the telescope and microscope, must be untrustworthy. His adversary, a Fellow of the newly-constituted Royal Society, countered by inquiring why we cannot write better with two pens than with a single one, since *Vis unita fortior.* It is to be noted that the experimentalists in their rejoinders always named Aristotle and Aristotelianism as the enemy, without attacking medieval philosophy in general; and indeed there was nothing in the tradition of Greathead and Roger Bacon and the Ockhamists to which they could or did object. The battle raged round the authority of Aristotle, for whom it was claimed that his doctrines were established and infallible certainties, and that he had had greater opportunities of acquiring knowledge than anyone of a later age could possibly have, since he did *totam peragrare Asiam;* while on the other side it was urged that the empty and talkative notionality of his philosophy had turned aside men of learning from the study of God's great book, universal Nature.

As time went on, the Aristotelians, getting the worst of these encounters, tended to withdraw from physics and cosmology, and to consolidate their philosophical position by claiming for metaphysics an almost complete independence of the observational sciences. Metaphysics, according to this interpretation, abstracts from all material things, and deals only with notions—the notion of Being in itself, its properties, unity, etc. Aristotle's physics might be out of date, but this could make no difference to the validity of his metaphysics. It was admitted that some perceptions must be received from the real sensible world in order to furnish the beginnings of knowledge, but these perceptions are of the most rudimentary character, such as are apprehended in early childhood—the perceptions that things come to be and cease to be, and that things actually existing are subject to constant change. It was held that metaphysics, working on this material, by sheer analysis discovers the notions of potency and act, and identifies change or motion or becoming as a passing from potency to act. There is no need for metaphysics to wait on any further discoveries of experimental physics: the simplest knowledge of the outside world enables the metaphysician to deduce certain immediate self-evident principles which rule absolutely every phenomenon that takes place in the real universe: the notions of potency and act have a metaphysical status which makes them superior to any merely physical doctrines. If a physical theory is inconsistent with the Aristotelian metaphysics, it cannot be admitted; because metaphysics is the supreme natural science, not physics. St. Thomas' Five Proofs of the existence of God are then defended from such attacks as that which William of Ockham had launched against the First Proof, by the assertion that they are essentially metaphysical in character, and therefore unaffected by any accessions to our scientific knowledge of the external world.

An obvious comment on this argument is that it robs St. Thomas of one of his chief titles to honor; the great service that he rendered to apologetics was precisely that he laid the emphasis on proofs which start from the concrete facts of the external world, as revealed by observation. A purely metaphysical proof of the existence of God is of little value for the practical purposes of apologetics, since most men will always be more ready to believe in God than to believe in any system of metaphysics. In fact, it may be said broadly that nobody has ever believed in any type of metaphysics leading to theism who did not believe in the theism before he believed in the metaphysics.

Moreover, the claim that metaphysics need not be based on anything but the most infantile kind of observation, breaks down on a closer examination. A science of all Being cannot afford to ignore any region of Being regarding which knowledge is available, even if its scrutiny requires special and difficult technique. Further, experimental physics differs from crude observation only in its degree of directness and in the amount of necessary rational interpretation, differences which are not qualitative. Again, it is generally recognized that molar behavior—the behavior of ordinary matter in bulk—

is to be explained as a statistical consequence of microscopic behavior—the behavior of atoms and molecules—which may be altogether different from molar behavior, so that the simple evidence of the senses may be misleading, and may need to be corrected by scientific knowledge before it is used. Modern physics, on the other hand, is based on *all* the available data, including innumerable experiences which were unknown until recently: that is, not only does it take account of the sense-data on which Aristotle based his metaphysics, but it also takes account of much that has been found in the last three centuries to be inconsistent with his conclusions; and out of all this material it constructs a self-consistent scheme of Nature, which supersedes the attempt to deduce physical consequences from metaphysical reasoning.

The impossibility of making a complete separation between Aristotelian metaphysics and the modern mathematical-experimental physics may be shown in many ways; and very clearly by the fact that certain phenomena can be described or explained in terms of both of them, and that the two explanations are in some cases contradictory.

Let us take as examples the transference of movement from a billiard cue into a ball, or the transference of heat from a fire into surrounding objects, or the passage of an electric current through a condemned criminal in an electric chair. The relevant doctrine of the Aristotelian-scholastic metaphysics is this: by its action, an agent arouses movement (*i.e.,* change) in a movable object from the state of potency to the state of act. Thus movement is *already* in a movable object, but in a state of potency; an agent (a mover) reduces the motion which is in potency to actual motion; hence motion does not pass from the mover to the moved. It is, indeed, impossible for any accident to pass from one thing into another thing, not only for the reason that during the passage the accident would cease to be an accident and become a substance, but because the heat of a fire, for example, is *this* heat and it gets its *thisness* from the subject in which it inheres, namely *this* fire: hence it is not conceivable that *this* heat, retaining its *thisness,* can become the accident of something else. Thus, according to the Aristotelian metaphysics, movement does *not* pass from the billiard cue into the ball, heat does *not* pass from fire into surrounding objects, and the electric current does *not* pass from the electrode of the chair into the criminal's body. The impossibility of reconciling such doctrines with modern physics cannot be ignored; and the principle that metaphysics is completely independent of physics is seen to be inconsistent with the facts.

21
The Cartesian revolution

Let us now turn our attention from the Aristotelians to their opponents, among whom was to be reckoned the only philosopher of the first rank living in the early seventeenth century. René Descartes, who was born in 1596, published his first important work, the *Discours de la Méthode,* only four years after the final trial of Galileo, and thereby inaügurated a new era in the history of speculative thought.

As a young man Descartes had become familiar with the scholasticism of the day; but it left him dissatisfied. Its conclusions were based principally on the affirmations of the great doctors; but the authority of the doctors was insecure, and the only branch of knowledge that seemed to be satisfactorily established was mathematics, whose procedure was to set out from self-evident postulates and to deduce from them results of practical value and incontrovertible truth. Descartes conceived the idea of searching for principles as certain as the axioms of mathematics, and on them as a foundation to rebuild philosophy.

In pursuance of this design, he proposed far-reaching changes in the philosophy of Nature. The first step—evidently suggested by the success of Kepler's work on the planetary orbits—was to describe the happenings of the external world in mathematical language. Now of all things presented to our observation, the spatial dimensions of bodies are the most obviously quantitative: he therefore laid hold of this feature, and based his system of the world on the affirmation that *the characteristic of matter is extension.* Another experience which is measurable is the passage of time; and hence the movement of bodies, which may be specified by the distance passed over in intervals of time, also admits of quantitative treatment. In terms of these two concepts, matter and movement, Descartes proposed to explain the physical universe: whenever possible, quality was to be made intelligible as varying quantity.

In this scheme, extension constitutes matter, and matter constitutes space, which is therefore a plenum: there is no void. The sensations of sound, light, heat, taste, and qualities generally, are to be regarded as belonging to our consciousness, and purely subjective: in Nature itself there is nothing but extension and the locomotion of its parts: the external world is a purely mechanical assemblage.

In the Cartesian transformation of philosophy, the very meanings of the key words were altered. Thus *motion,* which to the scholastics had meant change of any kind, was now restricted to mean change of position; *matter,* which in the older doctrine was correlative to *form,* now meant simply corporeal being. Especially noteworthy is the new importance acquired by *space* and *time.* The schoolmen had no word for "space" as we understand it; for *spatium* had rather the sense that "space" has in the Authorized Version of the Bible, *e.g.,* "All with one voice about the space of two hours cried out 'Great is Diana of the Ephesians' "[1]; while *locus* meant the space occupied by a particular body. *Where* and *when,* which to the scholastics had been merely two among the ten predicaments of Being, had come to dominate completely the description of Nature.

That description was even more strictly mechanical than the Newtonian description which later superseded it, as may

1 Acts xix. 34

be seen for instance in their respective conceptions of gravitation. Gravity had been classified by the schoolmen as an "occult quality"—that is to say, a force or tendency produced by no visible agency. Descartes denied the existence of occult qualities, and maintained (like the Greek atomists) that impact was the only mode in which one body could affect another; consequently he was compelled to furnish a new explanation of the fall of bodies toward the earth. This he did by postulating that surrounding the earth there is a vortex of subtle matter, or ether, which, by its pressure, provides the effect of gravity. Newton, on the other hand, formulated the inverse-square law without providing any mechanism to account for it; and in the preface to the second edition of the *Principia* there is a frank reversion to the scholastic view of gravity as an occult quality.

Thus in the picture of the world arrived at by Descartes, all the phenomena of astronomy and physics, so far as they were known at the time, were represented by aggregations or motions or pressures in the plenum of space. Nothing resisted his mechanical explanations, except the thought of man; this could not be brought into any relation with extension, and was evidently not amenable to mathematical analysis. It must therefore, he concluded, have a principle other than matter; and thus he arrived at a dualistic philosophy, and divided reality into the two great classes of extended and thinking substances, *res extensa* and *res cogitans,* the objective and the subjective, the corporeal and the spiritual world. As matter is characterized by extension, so the mind is characterized by thought: the two are completely independent, and no explanation of any relation between them is forthcoming.

The complete disjunction of the psychical from the physical which was characteristic of Cartesianism, has profoundly affected the subsequent history of science, and indeed of almost every department of human thought. In the first generation after Descartes there was an uneasy recognition of the possibility that—since any view of the cosmos must have a theological bearing—the new natural philosophy might prove harmful to religion; and in fact a keen controversy broke out on this very question. The dispute was centered around the doctrine of space, which rather suddenly underwent a profound change.

22
The Gassendi–Newton conception of space

The principal agent of the change was Pierre Gassendi (1592–1655), a friend of Galileo and Kepler, who rejected the Cartesian doctrine that space is a plenum, and reverted to the teaching of the Greek atomists regarding the void. In this system matter is not co-extensive with the whole of space, but is capable of movement *in* space, of which it occupies only a part. The importance of Gassendi is due to the fact that his principles were adopted by Newton, and thus became fundamental in classical physics. Space was now regarded as having a reality of its own, independent of its occupation by material bodies or of its perception by any human mind: it was infinite in extent and eternal in duration, and was the theater in which the drama of the universe was performed. Thus Newton declares that "absolute space, in its own nature, without regard to anything external, remains always similar and immovable,"[1] and "All things are placed in space as regards order of situation."[2] This had not been at all the point of view of scholasticism, and, as we shall see later, the recent progress of physical discovery has shown that it is radically unsound.

According to the Gassendi–Newton scheme, the events of the material world can all be reduced to the existence and motion of particles, which have location in space and some persistence in time. These particles can influence one another by means of mutual forces, which may be transmitted either by contact, as in collisions, or at a distance, as in the case of gravitation. The events which happen successively at any point of space can be arranged in order in a continuous sequence specified by a numerical variable called the "time," and it is always possible to say whether two events which take place at different points of space are, or are not, *simultaneous:* all observers, wherever they may be or however they may be moving, agree exactly in their estimates of simultaneity, so that the description of the flux of the universe in terms of

1 "Spatium absolutum, naturâ suâ sine relatione ad externum quodvis, semper manet similare et immobile," *Principia,* Schol. ad. Defin.

2 "In spatio quoad ordinem situs locantur universa," *ibid.*

space and time is completely free from subjective elements

The attempt to fit these concepts into the framework of philosophy and theology was confronted by the difficulty that besets all systems based on the Cartesian bifurcation between mind and matter—namely, that no provision is made for the interaction of spiritual with corporeal being. A possible solution seemed to be indicated by an idea put forward in 1647 by the Cambridge Platonist Henry More, that in some part of the human brain there is a *sensorium* or organ of internal sensation, where the understanding resides, to which the images of external things are conveyed by the organs of sense, and where they have a "tactual conjunction" with the soul, which thus perceives them. Newton now boldly suggested that space might be the sensorium of God. "Does it not appear from phenomena," he said,[3] "that there is a being incorporeal, living, intelligent, omnipresent, who in infinite space, as it were in his sensory, sees the things themselves intimately, and thoroughly perceives them, and comprehends them wholly by their immediate presence to himself?"

23
Is space finite or infinite?

The Newtonian doctrine that space is infinite dominated physics and cosmology for three centuries, from the rejection of the finite space of Aristotle to the introduction of the finite space of Eddington.

---
[3] *Opticks,* Qu. 28

Aristotle regarded the *place* of a body as being defined by the inner surface of a body containing it: bodies which are not contained in other bodies are not in any place, and therefore the first or outermost heaven is not in any place: space and time do not exist beyond it. He concluded that the total extent of the universe is finite.

When these views were discarded as a result of the work of Tycho and Kepler, the physical and astronomical schemes which succeeded them related entirely to happenings in that part of the cosmos in which we are situated: what happened at its farthest bound, and whether there was a farthest bound, were matters inaccessible to empirical determination or to theoretical calculation, and beyond fruitful conjecture: men of science very sensibly recognized that it is useless to think of the world as having a limited extent unless the limitation of its extent has some influence on observable phenomena.

There was, however, in the nineteenth century a certain amount of mathematical preparation for the later developments. The belief that Euclidean geometry—the geometry which is still taught in schools—was the only possible system of geometry, was shown to be unfounded: the discovery was made—and accepted, though only after a hard struggle against prejudice—that so far as logic is concerned, besides the Euclidean system, there are many other possible systems of geometry, each with its own rules: these were called *non-Euclidean* geometries; and since any one of them is as good as any other from the logical standpoint, the question as to which of them gave the correct account of the actual geometry of the world we live in, was a question that could be answered only by finding which of the theories best satisfied the observations.

The only kind of observations which could be of service in this matter were, of course, astronomical observations of the remotest bodies in the universe; for there is no appreciable difference between the systems of Euclidean and of non-Euclidean geometry until we consider geometrical figures of very great size. Observations of any value for this purpose have been made only in quite recent years: a brief explanation of them may be given at this point.

A hundred years ago astronomers believed that the stars and all celestial objects belonged to a single vast system, more or less in the shape of a lens, the central plane of the lens being roughly that of the Milky Way or Galaxy. Within the last half century it has become clear that millions of objects, which are visible in telescopes as nebulae, are outside the galactic system, and indeed are themselves independent galaxies; they are known as the *extra-galactic nebulae.* It is possible to estimate their distances, and also to determine the speed with which they are approaching us or retreating from us; and in the nineteen-twenties the remarkable fact was discovered that a tendency to approach is quite exceptional: practically all the extra-galactic nebulae are receding; and it was found moreover that the farther away they are, the greater are their velocities of recession. *The whole material universe is therefore continually expanding.* This empirical discovery of an expanding universe called for a theoretical explanation; and in 1930 Eddington showed that all the observed facts could be made intelligible as parts of a rational scheme if the cosmos were assumed to be non-Euclidean, with a certain value of the "curvature" (*i.e.,* the constant which distinguishes one non-Euclidean geometry from another). This entailed the conclusion that the universe is finite, having a volume which amounts to a certain definite number of cubic miles; it has not, however, any *boundary, i.e.,* there is no frontier across which there is something that does not belong to the finite universe. How the two attributes of finiteness and unboundedness can be reconciled, is a problem which presents no difficulty to a trained mathematician, but its exposition would take us too far afield here.[1]

24
Leibnitz's attack on Newtonianism

The idea that God had to be fitted into a scheme of which space, time, and matter were the primary concepts was attacked by Leibnitz, who rejected altogether the doctrine of absolute space and time having reality outside our minds, and maintained that space is only a conceptual entity, an

[1] The circumference of a circle is finite in length, but it is unbounded in the sense that a moving point which travels along it never comes up against a barrier, but can go round and round it forever. The combination of finiteness with unboundedness in a space is made possible by the space returning into itself.

order according to which situations are disposed, and time is only an order of succession. His argument against Newton may be put in a modern form somewhat as follows: During the operation of "summer time," the clock is an hour ahead of Greenwich time. This fact is, however, not made evident by any of the ordinary happenings of life, since all clocks, departures of railway trains, office hours, meal-times, and so forth bear to one another the same relations as before: in order to detect the change, we have to observe something which does not obey the Act of Parliament establishing summer time, such as the moment of sunset. Now suppose that some way could be found of compelling the heavenly bodies to adapt themselves to summer time on the same day as our clocks; then after this it would be impossible by any observations whatever to tell which kind of time we were keeping: the only evidence would be that furnished by memory—the recollection of the day that had only 23 hours, when the clocks were put forward. Let us now imagine that day to recede into the past, back to the creation of the world. Would there then be any difference between the two systems? Or, to put the same question in another form, is there any meaning in the statement that God might have created everything an hour sooner? Newton would say, Yes; Leibnitz would say, No. We may form our own judgment on the matter.

Another count in Leibnitz's indictment of Newtonianism related to the concept of *force,* the *vis motrix* of the *Principia,* which in the case of gravity was represented as acting at a distance. Now "force" in its statical sense, as for instance when we speak of "the force exerted by the weight of one pound," was a familiar idea to the schoolmen: their physics included what they called *scientia de ponderibus,* which dealt with such matters as the law of equilibrium of the lever, and the apparent weight of a body resting on an inclined plane. But the kinetic relations of force were unknown in the Middle Ages, and were first formulated in Newton's *Principia,* in the Second Law of Motion, which equates force to the product of mass and acceleration. Leibnitz rejected the whole idea. "Some men," he wrote, "begin to revive, under the specious name of *forces,* the *occult qualities* of the schoolmen; but they bring us back again into the Kingdom of Darkness."[1]

25

The law of gravitation and the Fifth Way

The new view of nature opened up by Newton's discovery of the law of gravitation made necessary certain changes in the presentation of St. Thomas' Fifth Way, the argument from the government of things. For St. Thomas, accepting the Aristotelian physics and cosmology, had before him the picture of the heavenly bodies being moved directly by intelligences, the admirable adjustment of their motions resembling the direction of an arrow by an archer, and so coming under the category of "government." The theory of gravitation now provided a complete specification of the behavior of the

[1] Letter of Leibnitz to Clarke, p. 265 of the correspondence (London, 1717).

planets, and indeed showed how to predict it for all time in the future, so that the idea of the motion being governed by intelligences possessing wills (with the thought hovering in the background that the wills might be free or even capricious) had to be abandoned. While this might call for some verbal changes in St. Thomas' reasoning, the argument as a whole was clearly strengthened rather than weakened; for the essence of it was to show that the phenomena point to the working of mind in the universe. Now the laws of Nature are not the causes but the representations of order; and the law of gravitation—a mathematical abstraction, existing only in the mental realm—provides a far clearer evidence of mind than was ever furnished by the hypothetical intelligences.

26
Newtonian determinism

In Newtonian physics, the changes that take place in the velocities of particles are due to forces which act between pairs of particles, the forces between the two members of any pair being (by Newton's Third Law of Motion) equal and opposite. The forces prominent in the earliest developments of the theory were the force of gravitation and the cohesive forces which bind aggregates of particles together as rigid bodies; but the scheme admitted of extension to forces of other types, such as those met with in electrostatic and magnetic phenomena. Newton showed how the known connection between forces and accelerations made it possible to write down equations by which the motion could be calculated. This of course implies that strict determinism holds over the whole domain of classical physics. Now determinism was nothing new, for the Aristotelian-scholastic system was deterministic; but between Newtonian and Aristotelian determinism there were significant differences. For Aristotle, the explanation of terrestrial movements is to be sought by looking beyond them to the majestic and orderly motions of the celestial bodies, and beyond them again to God, the unmoved mover and the ultimate originator of all that happens; and this is true not only in the material but also in the mental realm. In Newtonian physics on the other hand, the material world is regarded as an order closed in itself, whose future movement depends on nothing but its own initial state.

It was evidently harder for the Newtonian man to escape from this closed order, which is after all only a section of the universe, and to reach out to a God who stands outside it, than it was for St. Thomas to lead up to God through the open order of the Aristotelian physics, which comprehended the entire universe and had its natural terminus in Him. When the question of transferring St. Thomas' arguments to the domain of the new science was considered, the suggestion was made (as I have already explained) that this and other difficulties might be shelved by asserting that the Five Proofs are purely metaphysical, and are independent of any change in our conceptions of the external world; but I have given reasons for rejecting this solution, which can be definitely disproved, and which moreover abandons St. Thomas' fundamental aim of rising from Nature to God.

27
The postulate of causality

Newtonianism, like Aristotelianism, attempts to understand the world by tracing the connection of events with one another; and this is effected by ordering our experiences according to the category of cause and effect, discovering for every phenomenon its determining agents or antecedents. The affirmation that this connection is all-embracing, that no event happens without a cause, is the *postulate of causality.*

In the great breakaway from Aristotelianism in the seventeenth century, Aristotle's four causes were discarded with everything else. Descartes' claim, "Give me matter and motion, and I will construct the universe," amounted to a rejection of the notion of the formal cause; and none of the modern philosophers has attempted to develop the peripatetic doctrine in the light of the deeper knowledge of Nature which is now available. If Aristotle or St. Thomas had been alive, he would undoubtedly have risen to the occasion and seized the great opportunity; but their successors did nothing, and allowed their treatment of the subject to become more or less petrified in the form which it had assumed in the Middle Ages: probably many of them took the view that causality was a doctrine of metaphysics and that metaphysics was based on *a priori* assumptions and had nothing to learn from contact with the external world. Meanwhile the physicists, ignoring Aristotelianism altogether, and without any conscious intention of philosophizing, began to construct for themselves what amounts to a new metaphysic of causality: to this our attention must now be turned.

To begin with, they dropped the material, formal, and final causes (of which indeed most of them had never heard), and took the word *cause* to mean what Aristotle had called the "efficient cause." This could be typically represented by a dynamical force acting on a particle at a point. But with Newton's discovery of the law of gravitation the outlook became somewhat modified; for the most striking feature of Newtonian gravitation is that it is a reciprocal action—the two particles affect each other, and in exactly the same way. Thus, the notion of force tended to become replaced by the notions of *interaction* and of the *energy* possessed by the aggregate of a set of particles; and instead of considering single bodies under the influence of forces, the mathematical physicists developed theories such as that of Lagrange in dynamics, in which mathematical equations are obtained capable of predicting the future of a whole system of bodies simultaneously, without bringing in the ideas of "force" or "cause" at all. The tendency in this direction culminated in the year 1915, when the German mathematician David Hilbert of Göttingen showed that all physical happenings—gravitational, electrical, etc.—in the universe can be predicted from the knowledge of a single "world-function" as he called it, without any necessity to mention explicitly such things as forces or interactions between the bodies of which the universe is composed. Evidently the notion of a causal nexus, as affecting the relations between objects, has now completely disappeared, and has been replaced by the notion of a single entity governing the whole of existence. This is not far removed from the old doctrine of Malebranche, generally called *occasionalism* by philosophers, which asserted that created things have no proper activity of their own, but are merely *occasions* in respect of which the divine activity is manifested; the only modification being that in the metaphysical theory which the physicists have devised for themselves, God is no longer mentioned: He is replaced by a cosmic mathematical function.

While the word *cause* was in process of banishment from physics, the postulate of causality was also undergoing a revolutionary transformation. A scholastic might perhaps have formulated it thus:

> *Inceptive or contingent Being necessarily supposes its efficient cause*

—that is to say, "everything that is brought into existence necessarily supposes somebody or something to bring it into existence." Kant, in the second edition of his *Critique of Pure Reason,* adopts the form[1]:

> *All changes take place according to the law of the connection of cause and effect.*

---

[1] Kant regarded the principle of causality as not inherent in the external world in itself, but imposed by the nature of the human mind (*cf.* p. 108).

Modern philosophers have disputed as to whether the postulate of causality is an epistemological axiom, and in fact a necessary presupposition of all scientific knowledge (this was the view of Kant), or whether it is an induction from experience, being the fruit of our observation of habitual uniformities (this was the view of Hume). In any case, it is difficult to see that a statement of the postulate, however formulated, can be said to have a meaning until the word *cause* has first been defined, in terms either of other words whose meaning is known, or else of an observational procedure which is specified and which can be carried out. The physicists, taking no part in this discussion, fastened on the notion of *predictability* as being the essentially valuable content of the notion of causality, so far as their science was concerned; and accordingly they completed the postulate by embodying in it two fresh assumptions, namely, first, that when an effect is physical, its cause is an antecedent phenomenon of a purely physical character, and second, that the relation between measurable quantities in the two phenomena can be represented by mathematical formulae. The postulate could now be stated in the form: *The physical universe is a closed system, the succession of whose changes in time is, in principle at any rate, completely predictable.* When we take into account the finite speed of propagation of light, which is the greatest speed possible for the transmission of any kind of physical influence, the fundamental principle of classical physics can be finally stated thus: *It is possible to predict the physical conditions at any point* P *of the universe at any instant* t, *when we know the physical conditions, at any earlier instant* t_0, *at all points of space whose distance from* P *is not greater than* $c(t-t_0)$, *where* c *is the velocity of light.* This may be called the *Newtonian concept of causality.* This statement is more precise than any of the forms in which the postulate of causality has been expressed by philosophers.

28
The threat to causality from statistical physics

Meanwhile, however, a new unsettlement with regard to the principle of causality was appearing in a different quarter.

When the notion of a *cause* was first analyzed by Aristotle, the external world was known only in what would now be called its *molar* aspects; that is to say, matter was supposed to correspond to the appearance that it presents to the unaided eye, without any regard to the fine structure that has since Aristotle's time been revealed by the microscope or inferred from mathematical theory. Not until the nineteenth century did any great change in this respect take place: as the power of experimental and theoretical methods increased, knowledge regarding the structure of matter became more refined, and the homogeneity which the ancients assumed was found to be merely an effect of averaging, the underlying microscopic constitution being completely heterogeneous. According to the *kinetic theory of matter,* in any body which appears to the eye to be at rest, the smallest particles—atoms or molecules—are really in a state of irregular agitation. Thus, a gas such as ordinary air consists of enormous numbers of molecules—at the normal atmospheric pressure and at zero temperature centigrade there are about 2.7×10^{19} molecules per cubic centimeter—all rushing hither and thither, separated from one another in general by empty space, but frequently colliding. The "density" and "temperature" of the gas, which are definite quantities so long as we are dealing with an appreciable quantity of it, no longer mean anything when we are considering a single one of these moving molecules: it is only when we consider averages taken over an immense number of molecules that density and temperature come into existence.

The acceptance of the kinetic theory of matter raises some questions about the status of the laws of Nature. Consider for instance a metallic rod whose points are at different temperatures: then (neglecting the loss of heat to the external medium surrounding it) we have the law that the flow of heat at any point is proportional to the rate at which the temperature falls as we pass along the rod. As thus stated, this appears to be an ordinary causal law of Nature, like Newton's laws of motion. But we now see that it is really a statement about the average behavior of vast numbers of infinitesimal particles, whose individual behavior exhibits no regularity. All that we know about them are *probabilities*—for instance, the probability that the velocity of a particle, taken at random from the aggregate, lies between certain limits. How does this fit in with the principle of causality? Must the principle be replaced by statements about probabilities? If the notion of "necessity" was suggested to the ancients by the molar phenomena with which they were acquainted, must the notion be abandoned, at any rate over large domains of physics, now that we have a deeper understanding of what is actually happening?

To answer this question we must investigate the concept of probability as it occurs in physics. Consider, for instance, a phenomenon to which the idea of probability is usually attached, such as the tossing of coins or the casting of dice or the drawing of a card out of a pack. Here the issue is not predictable, and our *a priori* knowledge regarding it can be expressed only as a probability. How is this fact related to the principle of causality?

Until within the last few years, the reply to this inquiry would have been straightforward. It would have been pointed out that when we speak of physical events as being in all cases predictable, we mean that they are predictable *in principle*—that is, that they could be predicted by anyone who had an adequate acquaintance with the situation, an adequate knowledge of physical theory, and an adequate ability to perform mathematical calculations. In the case of tossing coins or throwing dice, we have not these qualifications for making the prediction: we have no accurate information as to the motion imparted to the coin by the act of tossing or to the die by the act of casting: we have as a rule no data regarding the resistance of the air or the moments of inertia of the coin or die, or the distance from the point of projection to the surface on which they will fall: and even if all this knowledge was in our possession, we could not carry out the laborious calculations required to determine the final issue, in the very short interval of time occupied by the passage of the coin or die through the air. But in classical physics, it is assumed that a being not hampered by any of these limitations would actually be able to make the prediction: for him, the event would be not one of chance, but of strict determinism.

Chance or probability, then, is (or was until recently believed to be) merely a word used to imply that in certain cases we are too ignorant to be able to do something which could be done by a being less ignorant than we are: the existence of chance, in this view, would not affect the statement that all events in the physical universe are governed by strict determinism. Later (§ 35) we shall find reason to conclude that such a position can no longer be maintained.

29
The Newtonians tend to deism

In 1692 Dr. Richard Bentley, the famous classical scholar, then engaged in preparing his Boyle lectures, *A confutation of Atheism,* applied to Newton for help in that part of the argument which related to physical science. Newton replied in four letters,[1] in which he expressed the opinion that the solar system was "not explicable by meer [*sic*] natural

[1] Printed in Horsley, *Isaaci Newtoni Opera* IV, p. 427.

causes," and that he was "forced to ascribe it to the counsel and contrivance of a voluntary agent." But the divine agency was apparently required only for the initial arrangement of the bodies: their subsequent behavior could be accounted for by the law of gravitation. After this, as appears from the controversy between Leibnitz and Dr. Clarke, there was a common tendency, in Newtonian circles, to conceive of the relation between God and the universe as analogous to that of a watchmaker to a watch which he has constructed, and which, having been set going, continues to function, for some time at any rate, without any necessity for the continued presence or attention of its originator. Such a conception led inevitably to the idea of an absentee God, who, having created the world, had left it to run its course without further divine intervention, and who was therefore for practical purposes non-existent. Leibnitz realized the dangers of this trend of thought, and saw that it is impossible to build any religion as a superstructure on a purely mechanical philosophy; and in particular that Christianity, being an incarnational and sacramental religion, is incompatible with any view of the universe which completely despiritualizes matter. Newton had adopted in essentials the impoverished representation of the objective world which Descartes had obtained by abstracting only its purely quantitative aspects: the result was a soulless mechanism, composed of parts which had no function except to move one another about in space, and with no relation to any conceptions of value or purpose.

30

Can the mathematicians predict new phenomena?

At the same time it must be recognized that as, in the development of physics, the laws become more general and more perfect, they begin to reveal a natural and ontological order, transcending the range of experimental facts on which they were based. Thus it becomes possible to assert from pure theory the existence of effects previously unknown: there have been striking cases in which a mathematician, working in his study without any contact with laboratories, has predicted the existence of wholly new and unexpected phenomena in the external world.

A typical example is Hamilton's discovery of conical refraction. If we mark a dot on a piece of paper, and look at it through a crystal of Iceland spar, we see in general not one dot but two: this is because the spar has the property called *double refraction.* In 1821 the French physicist Fresnel discovered the equation of the *wave-surface,* or locus at any instant of a disturbance generated at a particular point at some previous instant, in a doubly-refracting crystal; but he did not study the geometrical features of the surface as a mathematician would do. This was precisely what Hamilton did. He found that Fresnel's surface had some remarkable singularities, such as sharp peaks like the vertex of a cone, at each of which it had an infinite number of tangent-planes; and from the existence of these mathematical peculiarities in the wave-surface he inferred the existence of a corresponding optical phenomenon of a most amazing kind—namely, that a ray of light within the crystal would, under certain circumstances, be divided on emergence into an infinite number of rays, constituting a conical surface; while a single ray in air, incident on the crystal, might give a cone of rays inside the crystal. It should therefore be possible to arrange an experiment so that a dot on a sheet of paper, when viewed through a biaxial crystal, should appear not as two dots, but as a complete circle. This prediction was immediately verified.

Since the beginning of the twentieth century many novel and remarkable effects in physics have been discovered by mathematicians. Einstein's predictions of the bending of light-rays by the sun's attraction, and of the red-shift of spectral lines emitted in a strong gravitational field, are two notable instances. These were deduced from his general theory of relativity, which was entirely mathematical—that is to say, it did not originate in, or depend on, any new experiments or observations. Yet another striking discovery of the same type was the recognition that ordinary hydrogen gas is a mixture of two different kinds of molecules. Since for a century and a half hydrogen had been familiar to every schoolboy beginning science, and had been the subject of innumerable experiments by highly trained investigators, the announcement of its composite character not unnaturally came as a great surprise. The mathematical reasoning involved turned on a distinction which is made in algebra: if we have two algebraic quantities x and y, we can form from them certain expressions such as $x + y$, whose value is unaltered when x and y are interchanged with each other: these are said to be *symmetric* in x and y. We can also form expressions such as $x - y$, whose value is reversed in sign when x and y are interchanged; these are said to be *skew* in x and y. Now it was found, in 1927, that the mathematical equations which represent the conditions of existence of the hydrogen molecule possess two different solutions, of which one is symmetric and the other is skew. It followed that there must be two different kinds of hydrogen molecule, to which the names *para-hydrogen* and *ortho-hydrogen* were given. These two tautomers behave in exactly the same way as regards the formation of chemical compounds, which explains why the chemists had never distinguished or separated them; but the specific heat of para-hydrogen is greater at low temperatures than that of ortho-hydrogen; and their boiling-points and conductivities are also different. Hydrogen gas prepared by the usual chemical processes consists of one-quarter para-hydrogen and three-quarters ortho-hydrogen.

Physical theory, then, is much more than a mere account of the course of observed phenomena: because the world is rational, the different effects are so inter-connected logically that when we have found by observation a certain number of them, we can deduce the others by pure reasoning without making any fresh observations. Our reason is capable of establishing between abstract notions, relations corresponding to true relations between things: physics, at first purely descriptive, eventually becomes asymptotic to a metaphysics.

31

The downfall of the Gassendi–Newton concept of space

The enlargement of scientific knowledge in the last half century has brought to light certain defects in the Newtonian system, and some radical changes have taken place in the representation of Nature. I propose now to describe these and to discuss their bearing on the arguments for theism.

The first serious trouble arose in connection with the doctrine of space. The space of Gassendi and Newton was, so far as geometry was concerned, the space of Euclid: it was infinite, homogeneous, and completely featureless, one point being just like another: so far as physics was concerned, it was like the vacuum of the ancient atomists, mere emptiness into which things could be put. From the philosophical point of view this concept was open to the objection that Aristotle had urged against the doctrine of the atomists: namely, that if space were devoid of local properties, the tendency of a body to move spontaneously in a particular direction (*e.g.,* the existence of a gravitational field, as we should say) would be unintelligible. As a matter of fact, the successors of Newton felt this difficulty; and, having started with a space that was in itself simply nonentity having no property except a capacity for being occupied, they proceeded to fill it several times over with ethers designed to provide electric, magnetic, and gravitational forces, and to account for the propagation of light; and as it was impossible to draw any effective distinction between these ethers and space, Newtonian space became eventually a plenum of the most elaborate kind, possessing such qualities as density and rigidity everywhere. Its points admitted of individual identification, and could be regarded as fixed; and having thus acquired a more definite and concrete substantiality than Newton himself had ever contemplated, its absolute character became an essential and inseparable axiom of classical physics. But the discovery in 1905 of the principle of relativity led to inferences incompatible with the existence of any kind of quasi-material ether; and thus the Gassendi–Newton doctrine became involved in hopeless contradiction.

32
Curved space

The problem that now confronted physicists was this: how can local properties, such as a gravitational field, exist in space, when the existence of an ether is not a permissible supposition? The answer was furnished in 1915 by the *General Theory of Relativity* of Einstein. He discarded Gassendi's assumption that space was a uniform characterless vacuum, and postulated that it had a property of *curvature,* varying from point to point; and that just as (to make use of a rough analogy) a paramagnetic body when placed in a magnetic field tends to move from the weaker to the stronger places in the field, so a massive body in space might be pictured as moving from places of weak to places of strong curvature. The curvature, in fact, performs in General Relativity the same kind of function as the density and rigidity of the ether did in classical physics; but, unlike the ether properties, it does not come into conflict with the principle of relativity. In Einstein's conception, space is no longer the stage on which the drama of physics is performed: it is itself one of the performers; for gravitation, which is a physical property, is entirely controlled by curvature, which is a geometrical property of space.

In Einstein's theory of gravitation, the Newtonian concept of force is completely done away with: a free particle moves in a path determined solely by the curvature properties of space. The changes of position of the particle, in their turn, bring about changes in the curvature of space, so that the particle and space together may be regarded as a single system, whose evolution is determined by the law that the total curvature of space-time is to be a minimum; as we may say, *gravitation represents a continual effort of the universe to straighten itself out:* a statement so completely teleological that it would have delighted the hearts of schoolmen.

33
The unobservable transitions

While classical physics was thus being undermined by the principle of relativity, an even more devastating attack on it was developing from the side of quantum theory. In 1913 a young Danish research student named Niels Bohr, working under Rutherford in Manchester, published some new and revolutionary ideas regarding the way in which light is generated. Let us take as the simplest example the generation of light by a hydrogen atom. This atom consists of a massive particle in the center, with an electron circulating around it, just as the earth and the other planets move around the sun. Now in the solar system a planet may revolve at any distance whatever from the sun—that is to say, there is no restriction on the dimensions of the planetary orbits; and similarly according to classical physics, the electron in the hydrogen atom might revolve at any distance whatever from the nucleus: the possible orbits would form a continuous sequence. Bohr, however, now put forward the suggestion that this deduction from classical physics was false, and that, in fact, only certain particular orbits are allowable: just as if in the solar system a planet could move in the orbit of the earth, or in that of Mars, or Jupiter, but could not move in any orbit intermediate between these, such as the orbits in which the minor planets actually do move. When the electron is moving in one of the permitted orbits, the atom is said to be in a *stationary state;* and the fundamental assumption of Bohr's theory is that the atom, when it is not emitting light, must always be in one or other of the stationary states, without the possibility of its being in any intermediate condition. The emission of light takes place when, and only when, the atom changes from one stationary state to another stationary state.

Bohr showed that his suggestion would explain many of the known features of spectra most admirably; but some serious objections could be brought against it; and one of them was, that he could give no explanation of the process by which an atom in a state A is raised or lowered to another state B. In the change, the electron must transfer itself from the orbit belonging to state A to the orbit belonging to state B; and according to the Gassendi–Newton doctrine, an object such as an electron can transfer itself from one position to another position only by traveling over the space between them, occupying in succession the whole continuous sequence of intermediate positions. Bohr, however, found it impossible to provide any description of the transference of the electron, and was compelled to renounce the attempt to explain transitions between stationary states. At the time this was regarded as an imperfection in his work, but today we take a very different view, and regard Bohr's renunciation as one of the most valuable and permanent features in his theory, and as a landmark in the history of science; for the subsequent development of quantum-mechanics has shown that his inability to trace the adventures of the electron between leaving orbit A and settling in orbit B was not due to any insufficiency on his part, but was inherent in the physical situation.

What is the difficulty? Is it that the mathematical operations required to calculate the motion are so intricate as to be beyond the skill of the best mathematicians? Or is it that owing to the imperfections of our laboratory apparatus we cannot make measurements of sufficient delicacy to specify empirically the successive stages of the motion? No, the trouble is much more deeply seated. Even if we could imagine an investigator capable of solving any set of mathematical equations whatever, and, moreover, possessing instrumental equipment of the highest refinement conceivable, even then the problem of depicting in terms of the concepts of classical physics the transition of the atom from one stationary state to another would be insoluble; and the reason is, that the process cannot be described as a continuous movement of an electron in space; we are confronted by a theoretical impossibility, like the impossibility of expressing π as a rational fraction, or the impossibility of constructing a regular heptagon with ruler and compasses.

The importance of this discovery is that it invalidates the presuppositions of the whole Gassendi–Newton doctrine: it shows that there are events in the physical world which cannot be represented on the background of space and time.

34
The newer epistemology of physics

It therefore becomes necessary to find a metaphysics different from that which has been associated with classical physics; for metaphysics must originate with reference to physics, since it is the conceptual framework into which our experience of Nature is to be fitted. The progress of science has destroyed the foundations on which the Newtonian natural philosophy has been grounded. How is the damage to be repaired?

Evidently space and time must be deposed from the dominant position which they held in Newtonianism, and relegated to a lower status. A system of physics has been proposed by the late Sir Arthur Eddington, in which this principle is carried out by introducing sixteen "symbolic coefficients," in terms of which all physical facts can be expressed; of these coefficients, three correspond to the three dimensions of space and one corresponds to time, but they are on much the same footing as the other twelve coefficients, which correspond to such physical entities as electric charge and moment, magnetic force, etc. With these assumptions, certain otherwise puzzling facts fall into their places as elements of a rational coherent structure. Take, for example, the fact that all electrons have the same electric charge. For this, the classical theory of electricity has no explanation to offer; the law of interaction is that two electrified particles repel each other with a force proportional to the product of their charges and inversely proportional to the square of the distance between them; and this law is valid whether the charges are equal or unequal. Yet it is impossible to believe that the actual equality of the charges of electrons is a mere accident; it must be fundamental in the scheme of Nature, and there must be a reason for it. How fundamental and necessary it is has been shown by a study of the forces by which atoms are held together so as to form molecules. Take for instance the hydrogen molecule, which is constituted of two hydrogen atoms, each atom consisting of a nucleus and an electron. If the two electrons are interchanged with each other, there is no change in the system, since the electrons are identical: from which feature of the situation, by following up its consequences in the light of quantum-mechanics, we can predict that a stationary state of the system exists, which has less energy than the energy of the two atoms when separated: this stationary state corresponds to the stable hydrogen molecule.

In the proof, everything turns on the exact equality of the two electrons: if they had different charges, the binding force (which is purely quantum-mechanical) would not exist; and this is true of all those binding forces which in chemistry are called "homopolar bonds." Thus the world would be a very different place from what it is, if all electrons were not identical. In the Eddingtonian scheme, not only is the equality of charge of all electrons an essential concept, but the actual charge is evaluated by purely theoretical methods.

But the matter is not yet exhausted; there is something more profound: electrons are indistinguishable in a still more rigorous sense. If two electrons are at one instant at places A and B, and at a later instant at places C and D, it is impossible to say which of the electrons at C and D is the one that was formerly at A; that is to say, an electron can freely exchange its recognizability with other electrons: it has no sameness of being, no proper identity, no separate history. Its selfhood is merged in an electronhood which it shares with all other electrons. From the philosophical point of view this is clearly important, for it necessitates a revision of the concept of individuality as applied to the elementary particles, and reopens, in connection with the most recent discoveries in physics, the question which engaged so much attention in the Middle Ages, regarding the nature of *universals* or general terms, which represent the common basis of a class of individual objects.

The transition which is now in progress, from classical physics to a new natural philosophy conformable to relativity and quantum-mechanics, is less violent than that which took place three centuries ago, when classical physics arose on the ruins of Aristotelianism; but it may prove not less significant.

35
The quantum theory and the postulate of causality

One of the most fundamental changes is with regard to determinism: it must now be explained how in recent years a careful analysis, by the aid of the new science of quantum-mechanics, of certain phenomena in atomic physics, has shown that the postulate of causality is not universally valid.

It is well known that radioactive substances, of which radium is the type, emit radiations of various kinds continually and spontaneously. These radiations proceed from the nuclei of the atoms of the substance, which, in the act of sending out radiation, break up and become nuclei of other elements; thus when an atom of radium emits an alpha-particle, the atom becomes an atom of radium emanation. Not all the atoms in a lump of a radioactive substance break up at the same instant, and thus a perpetual succession of emissions is kept up until every atom of the substance has been transformed—a process which may take thousands of years. If a small quantity of a radium salt is placed near a fluorescent screen, the alpha-particles shot out by the radium bombard the screen, producing scintillations which may be observed. These scintillations appear at irregular intervals, and the instants when they will be seen cannot be predicted, since we have no means of foretelling when any particular radium atom will explode. The phenomenon thus belongs to the category of "chance," and we have to inquire what is the nature of "chance" in this case: has it the same meaning as in the tossing of coins and casting of dice—that is to say, is our inability to predict the instant of the next scintillation due merely to the limitation of our powers of observation and calculation, so that a Being better equipped than we are would be able to make the prediction—or, on the other hand, is there a real and inescapable uncertainty, so that an imaginary physicist, endowed with faculties of human type but immensely more powerful and acute, could do no better than we can?

This problem has been solved only as the result of a profound discussion of the mathematical theory of radioactivity: an elementary account is given in a Guthrie lecture which I gave to the Physical Society of London in 1943,[1] and the complete analysis is to be found in Professor von Neumann's book, *Mathematische Grundlagen der Quanten-Mechanik:* the answer is quite definite, and is in favor of the second of the alternatives; that is, the time of break-up of a radium atom is unpredictable not merely in practice, but in principle[2]: there is a genuine indetermination, a failure of the postulate of causality. The view of Kant, that the postulate is a necessity of thought, independent of all experience, is thus definitely disproved; and a striking illustration is thereby provided of the dependence of metaphysical axioms on observational facts. Even if it is granted that the fundamental conceptions of science—cause, order, relation, identity, class—are metaphysical, they do not constitute knowledge, until their content has been filled in from experience.

Although the time of the explosion of a particular radium atom is unpredictable, it must not be supposed that there is a complete absence of law in connection with the phenomenon. The law, however, becomes manifest only when we consider a finite quantity of a radium salt containing many billions of atoms: a certain proportion of the atoms that are

[1] *Proc. Phys. Soc.* 55 (1943) 459

[2] The proof assumes the truth of the fundamental principles of quantum-mechanics; but to deny these, to the degree required, would involve us in difficulties which seem insuperable.

in existence, unexploded, at the beginning of any year, will explode during the year; and this fraction is always the same whatever year we choose, and is characteristic of the element radium: it is, in fact, 4.1×10^{-4}. From it we can calculate that the *average* life of a radium atom is 2,440 years. This is an example of a *statistical* regularity, such as was discussed in §28.

36
The principle of uncertainty

In the comparatively new quantum-theory of physics, the differences between molar behavior and microscopic behavior, to which reference was made in §28, confront us at every turn. Many of the differences can be traced to a change in ideas which has been found to be necessary with regard to the concept of a *particle.* The particle of the Newtonian natural philosophy was simply a lump of ordinary matter, considered as reduced indefinitely in size: at any instant it had a definite location in space and a definite velocity; mathematically speaking, it was a moving geometrical point. Quantum-theory, however, has shown that there are difficulties in assigning to any object a definite location and a definite velocity at the same time; the matter may be illustrated by an analogy taken from music.

Let us imagine an experimental arrangement in which a musical note is produced by an organ pipe, controlled by a key, so that the sound is emitted when the key is pressed down, and is cut off instantly when the key is released. The note will be supposed to be a pure tone,[1] and we shall suppose that its rapidity of vibration, or frequency (which determines the pitch), is v, very low in the scale, so that the number of oscillations per second is comparatively small. Then, when the experiment is performed, the question "At what instant was the note of frequency v sounded?" does not admit of a precise answer, since the sound would actually extend over the appreciable interval of time while the key was down. In order to obtain as nearly as possible a note sounded at a precise instant, let us shorten its duration as much as possible, releasing the key a fraction of a second after it has been depressed. In this way we can increase the precision of the statement regarding the time of the sound; but, by doing so, we cut short the train of oscillations; and if we imagine the duration of the note shortened so much that less than a single complete oscillation takes place, the sound will no longer produce on the ear the sensation of a definite pitch: it can no longer be described as a frequency v.

Thus the two requirements, that the sound should be emitted at a definite instant and that it should be of a definite pitch, are incompatible with each other: the more nearly instantaneous we can make the note, the less pure is its tone.

This inability to specify exactly and simultaneously all the quantities involved is characteristic of every phenomenon which, like musical notes, depends on wave-motions: if we

[1] *i.e.,* speaking mathematically, a simple harmonic oscillation of the air.

wish to determine the rapidity of vibration, or frequency, of the motion, then it is necessary to observe the succession of undulations over an appreciable interval of time, and it is therefore impossible to specify any one instant as the "instant at which the measurement was obtained."

Similar insuperable obstacles to precise statement are found everywhere in atomic physics, and are the cause of a certain haziness or blurred definition which is now known to be exhibited by all elementary effects in Nature. It may be shown that physical quantities generally are associated in pairs, such that an increase of accuracy in knowledge regarding one member of a pair necessarily entails a decrease of accuracy in knowledge regarding the other member.

In particular, we cannot specify both the location and the velocity of an electron simultaneously with precision; and thus electrons, and indeed all the other elementary constituents of the universe—protons, positrons, etc.—are not particles in the Newtonian sense: if the location is accurately determined, then the velocity cannot be known; and conversely, if the velocity is known accurately, then we cannot say where the entity is situated. This uncertainty is diminished, and indeed becomes altogether negligible, when we are dealing with lumps of matter of appreciable size, which are constituted of very large numbers of protons and electrons; and therefore it was not dreamt of until physical investigation was carried into the atomic domain. But all our philosophical notions of the nature and behavior of matter were derived originally from experiences with molar material; and we are therefore faced with the necessity for a re-examination, and possibly some alteration, of those notions, as a result of our new knowledge about the elementary constituents of the world.

37
The age of the world

Many of the factors that have contributed to form the modern conceptions of the world we live in have arisen from recent developments in astronomy and astrophysics, in particular from the investigations regarding the age of the universe.

We have already explained (§23) the expansion of the universe, as a result of which the distance between any two galaxies is doubled in about 1,300 million years. If we reverse this process in order to find what has happened in the past, we find that the galaxies must have been all crowded together in a comparatively small region at some time between 10^9 and 10^{10} years ago. This is only one of many ways in which recent researches have led to the conclusion that the universe cannot have existed for an infinite time in the past, at any rate under the operation of the laws of Nature as we know them: there must have been a beginning of the present cosmic order, a creation as we may call it, and we are even in a position to calculate approximately when it happened. One way of arriving at an estimate is to study the energy of stars, regarding them, so to speak, as gigantic fires in which heat-energy is continually being produced, more or less as it is produced in a fire by the combustion of coal (though the reactions in stars are very different from those in terrestrial fires), while there is also unceasingly a loss of energy by radiation from the surface of the star into space. The processes by which the heat-energy is generated are now understood to a degree which makes them amenable to a rough computation, leading to the conclusion that the age of a typical star can scarcely exceed 10^{10} or 10^{11} years.

A different line of approach is to study the history of associated groups of stars, such as the Pleiades and the Hyades in the constellation Taurus. The Pleiades form a cluster of about 200 stars, comparatively isolated in space, and occupying a volume which may roughly be described as a sphere whose radius is ten light-years. The individual stars have motions distributed at random, so that the distribution of stars around any particular one of them is continually changing. Consequently the gravitational force acting on the star is subject to fluctuations; and a mathematical analysis of the situation shows that the cumulative effect of the fluctuations over a long period of time—millions of years—is to cause stars to escape from the group, and thus to lead to the dispersal and disintegration of the cluster. For any given cluster, it is possible to calculate what may be called its *average life:* this is defined as an interval of time such that in it the probability that a particular star will have escaped is 0.63: in the case of the Pleiades, the average life has been calculated by Chandrasekhar to be about 3×10^9 years. Since many clusters of this type are known, it would seem that the age of the universe must be a quantity roughly of this order of magnitude.

A further estimate of the age of the universe is provided by a study of double stars. In this case the gravitational forces due to other stars in the neighborhood are different for the two stars of a pair, and in a long period of time the difference will cause the dissolution of their partnership. The working out of this idea has led to an estimate of about 5×10^9 years for the time elapsed since the beginning of the process.

These different estimates converge to the conclusion that there was an epoch about 10^9 or 10^{10} years ago, on the further side of which the cosmos, if it existed at all, existed in some form totally unlike anything known to us: so that it represents the ultimate limit of science. We may perhaps without impropriety refer to it as the Creation. It supplies a concordant background to the view of the world which is suggested by the geological evidence, that every organism ever existent on the earth has had a beginning in time. If this result should be confirmed by later researches, it may well come to be regarded as the most momentous discovery of the age; for it represents a fundamental change in the scientific conception of the universe, such as was effected four centuries ago by the work of Copernicus.

38
The introduction of absolute time

Physicists and astronomers in the past have thought of the world as continuing from age to age, one second of time being not essentially different physically from any other: as a consequence of the new outlook, time may henceforth be measured from a *natural origin* of time.

There is a close parallel to this in the history of ideas about temperature. The early physicists thought of temperature as something which could increase or decrease continuously to an indefinite extent, one degree of temperature being not essentially different from any other; but in the nineteenth century it was shown that at about —273° centigrade there is an *absolute zero* below which the temperature of a body can never fall. This constitutes a *natural origin* for temperature: if the temperature measured from this origin is called the *absolute* temperature, then it is found that the absolute temperature enters into many physical laws; for instance, the amount of energy radiated away in one second by (say) a red-hot poker is proportional to the fourth power of its absolute temperature; or again, at any temperature the ratio of the thermal conductivity (*i.e.,* the readiness to conduct heat) to the electric conductivity (*i.e.,* the readiness to conduct electricity) is approximately the same for all metals, and the value of this ratio is therefore proportional to the absolute temperature.

Similarly, if *absolute time* is measured from the natural origin of time (the Creation), it may be that the absolute time will enter into some laws of Nature. Nothing is definitely known about this, but various speculations have been published by reputable physicists. According to one of them, the Newtonian "constant" of gravitation is not constant but is continually decreasing, in inverse proportion to the absolute time; and the same hypothesis leads to the conclusion that there is a continuous generation of new matter in the universe, the total number of protons in the universe increasing proportionally to the square of the absolute time. According to a different speculation, the "constant" of gravitation is continually *increasing*, proportionally to the absolute time. In Eddington's theory, both the Newtonian constant of gravitation and the number of protons in the universe remain invariant in time.

The Creation itself, being a unique event, is of course outside science altogether.

39
The Creation and the Five Ways

From the point of view of Natural Theology, the insertion of a creation into the scientific picture of the cosmos is an event of immense importance. St. Thomas doubtless realized what a powerful argument for the existence of God could be built up if it could be shown by pure reason based on observation that the universe had a definite beginning in time. But in the thirteenth century scientific cosmogony was as yet unborn, and, as is well known, St. Thomas held that the belief of Christians in a creation was based on revelation, and could not be established independently by the means of rational science.[1]

Now that it actually has been established, we can return to the Five Ways, and in particular to the second one, the proof from causality. It will be necessary first to look more closely into some properties of the relation of cause and effect.

Suppose that B is the cause of an effect A, that C is the cause of B, that D is the cause of C, and so on; the events A, B, C, D, . . . form a *chain.* In St. Thomas' proofs we have many cases of chains of this kind; thus in the First Proof the chain is formed by entities, each one of which is the mover of the entity immediately preceding.

St. Thomas always supposes these chains to extend, link after link, until they find their terminus in God. But the branch of mathematics known as topology (or, for that matter, commonsense) teaches us that a chain can behave in many different ways; for instance, a chain might be *closed:* B might be the cause of A, C the cause of B, D the cause of C, E the cause of D; but what is to prevent A from being the cause of E? In that case, A, B, C, D, E would form a closed ring, a re-entrant system. If, however, a chain of causes is re-entrant, the proof that it must terminate in God evidently breaks down; it does not, in fact, terminate anywhere. Is it a

[1] *Summa Theol.* I q. 46 a. 2

defect in St. Thomas' proofs, that he does not secure his chains against re-entry?

In order to answer this question we must go to the mathematicians and ask them what conditions a relation (such as the relation of cause and effect) should satisfy, in order that we may be guaranteed against the occurrence of re-entry in the chains formed by the relation.

It is easy to see that certain kinds of relations cannot form re-entrant chains. Suppose for instance that the entities considered are numbers, and that the relation considered is the relation "greater than." If a number B is greater than a number A, and C is greater than B, and D is greater than C, and E is greater than D, then it is plainly impossible that A should be greater than E; that is, the relation "greater than" cannot form a re-entrant chain. To take another example, suppose that the entities considered are musical sounds, and that the relation in question is the relation of being one semitone higher in pitch, so that the note B is a semitone higher than the note A, the note C is a semitone higher than B, D is a semitone higher than C, and so on; then it is clearly impossible that the chain A, B, C, D, . . . can ever be re-entrant. The general rule is that a relation cannot form re-entrant chains if some quantity, or measurable quality, associated with the entities always increases (or always decreases) as we pass from one entity to the next beyond it in the chain. The relation is then said by the mathematicians to be *strictly monotonic.* Such a relation cannot form a re-entrant chain.

Now, the remarkable thing is that St. Thomas did actually secure that his relations should be strictly monotonic. Listen to what he says in the *Compendium Theologiae*[2]: "*Videmus enim omnia quae moventur, ab aliis moveri, inferiora quidem per superiora: sicut elementa per corpora coelestia, et in elementis quod fortius est, movet id quod debilius est: et in corporibus etiam coelestibus, inferiora a superioribus aguntur.*" That is to say, in Aristotle's cosmology, the cause of events on one of the celestial spheres is to be found in the next sphere outside it, so that the chain of causes corresponds to the orderly arrangement of the spheres: the relation he is considering is strictly monotonic, because the second member of the relation is, in this sense, always "superior" to the first. Our original fear, that St. Thomas might have overlooked this matter, is therefore unjustified. But, alas! his solution is completely bound up with the discredited Aristotelian physics,[3] and cannot now be accepted; so at this point the proof, in its original form, is defective, and the argument can be brought into harmony with modern knowledge only by a restatement. Happily, the progress of science has made possible a restatement which not only restores the cogency of the general argument of the Second Proof, but may be regarded as strengthening it,

The question is, can it be proved that in modern physics, the relation of cause and effect is a strictly monotonic rela-

[2] Caput III, *Quod Deus sit,* and Caput IV, *Quod Deus est immobilis*

[3] This illustrates the fact that the proofs are not purely metaphysical, but depend essentially on physics.

tion? The answer is furnished by reference to the law that no physical influence can be transmitted at a greater speed than the velocity of light *in vacuo;* a law which, though actually first enunciated by Einstein, may be regarded as a natural development of classical theory. This law ensures that when one body causes an effect of any kind in another body which is not coincident with it, the cause precedes the effect *in time.* Moreover the doctrine that molar bodies are built up of elementary particles which are separated from one another by empty space, eliminates the possibility of a breakdown of the argument through the coincidence of bodies. Thus we see that the cause-effect relation is strictly monotonic, that a chain of causes and effects can never be re-entrant, but must be extended indefinitely as an open chain of antecedents and successors in time.

St. Thomas' argument then requires us to consider what happens to this chain at its remote end. Does it continue backward to negative eternity, or does it terminate at some definite epoch in the past? St. Thomas had to face the difficulty of proving that the chain cannot have an infinite regress, but must have a terminus: this difficulty now disappears automatically, since the chain cannot in any case be prolonged backward beyond the Creation. At this point we escape from the order of the Newtonian cosmos, and, as in St. Thomas' original proof, the sequence of causes terminates in God.

In the argument as usually presented the language used is appropriate to the case when each effect has only one cause, and each cause has only one effect, so that all chains of causation are simple linear sequences. If we now take into account the fact that an effect may be produced by the joint action of several distinct causes, and also that a cause may give rise to more than one effect, the chains of causation may be branched, and also may have junctions with one another; but since the rule still holds, that the cause always precedes the effect in time, it is evident that the proof is not essentially affected. Moreover, the argument does not require that all chains of causation, when traced backward, should terminate on the *same* ultimate point: in other words, it does not lead necessarily to the conclusion that the universe acquired its entire stock-in-trade in a single consignment at the Creation, and that it has received nothing since. Thus it does not warrant the view, so common among the deistic Newtonians of the eighteenth century, that the system of the world is absolutely closed and has developed according to purely mechanical laws, so that all the events of history must have been implicit in its specification at the primeval instant. On the contrary, the recent trend of physical thought (as will be evident from what has been said about the principle of causality) is in favor of the view that in the physical domain, there is a continual succession of intrusions or new creations. The universe is very far from being a mere mathematical consequence of the disposition of the particles at the Creation, and is a much more interesting and eventful place than any determinist imagines.

Over the field within which rational science is possible, there must be regularity, for on this we depend for a connection between the past, the present, and the future; but the regularity is not universal and exhaustive, for the world is being enriched unceasingly by the accession of new elements. It has been surmised that some relation, unknown to us as yet, may exist between the intrusions and the regularities: C. S. Pierce, the American mathematician and philosopher, believed that the laws of nature have resulted from an evolutionary process, the fixing of inveterate habits, so to speak, in the world of inanimate matter. But however this may be, the way in which the two features of regularity and novelty are ensured simultaneously, and in both the physical and the psychical spheres, compels our wonder and exaltation.

40
The Fifth Way

There is one notable respect in which the attitude of the schoolmen to the external world differed from that which has been general since the Renaissance, namely that the scholastics tried to understand the purpose behind events, whereas the later effort has been directed toward discovering laws rather than ends, *how* rather than *why*, and has renounced the claim to understand the deeper significance of its own discoveries. Reverting to Aristotle's doctrine of the four kinds of causes, we may say that in modern theoretical physics, the formal and efficient causes of physical events have been absorbed, and in a certain sense blended, in the mathematical theory, while the existence of a final cause has been simply ignored. It is in the light of this difference between the attitudes of the thirteenth and the twentieth century that we have to consider the Fifth Way, the proof from order, purpose, and function.

St. Thomas set out from the assumption that inanimate objects, such as are considered in physics, behave as if striving to accomplish some purpose; whence he inferred that they must be directed by an intelligent Being, whom he identified with God. The physics of our age does not make St. Thomas' initial assumption; and it would therefore appear that the argument must be developed from a somewhat different beginning. To obtain a starting-point for the reconstruction, we have to consider what it is in the modern outlook that has taken the place of the medieval idea.

We recognize now—even more fully than our ancestors—that there is order, system, adjustment, fitness in the nature of things and in their relations to other things; the eye, for instance, is highly organized and is adapted for seeing. So far as order is concerned, our knowledge is vastly greater than it was in the thirteenth century, for we have attained the concept of a mathematical structure embracing the entire universe. The world is a system for which predictions can be made, a cosmos, not a chaos. Facts revealed by experience have a character of rationality: mathematics, abstract thought, has the power of solving concrete problems of physics.

Between the medieval and the modern conceptions, however, there is not so much difference as appears at first sight. To say that natural objects, though not endowed with consciousness, behave as if they were striving to accomplish some purpose, is, after all, only a naive and picturesque way of saying that their behavior is not lawless and haphazard, but is governed by definite rules; and for the purposes of St. Thomas' argument one of the two formulations of the initial assumption is practically as good as the other. Mathematical law is a concept of the mind; and from the existence of mathematical law it is not unreasonable to infer that there is a mind, analogous to our minds, in or behind material Nature: the order which exists is meant to exist; and we make this inference on exactly the same grounds as we infer the possession of minds and intentions by other human beings. When we reflect on the unity of the cosmos—its coherence and interconnectedness, the adaptation and co-ordination of its parts—we are led to consider that it exists for some intelligible end. In a world that was not the expression of intelligence, science could never have come into being.

Moreover, the fact—which was not known to St. Thomas—that the *same* mathematical laws are valid over the cosmos—that it is shown by science to be interrelated and consistent—leads to the inference that there is only a *single* mind involved in the whole creation; so that in this approach to the conception of God, modern science, by excluding polytheism, actually supplies an important corollary to St. Thomas' proof.

To put the argument in different words: just as we recognize that there are other bodies besides our own and these bodies constitute the material universe, so we recognize that there are other minds besides our own, and in particular that there is a mind, akin to our minds, whose operations are revealed in the behavior of non-living matter—the laws of Nature—and this mind is One over the entire universe, whose totality is thus bound into a unity. The proof from order is today more complete, more comprehensive, and more majestic than in the form presented in the thirteenth century.

The argument up to this point does not distinguish between a transcendent and an immanent mind, between theism and pantheism. But here again modern science supplies a criterion which was not available to St. Thomas, for if we have the knowledge that the universe cannot have existed for an infinite time in the past under the operation of our present laws of Nature—in other words, that there must have been a Creation—and moreover that there must come a time when for physical reasons life will be impossible, then these are facts which make it incredible to suppose that God is bound and conditioned by a world which has its appointed times of birth and death. If we have in any way arrived at the conviction that God exists, modern cosmology points to the further conclusion that He must be, in one aspect at least, extramundane.

Kant objected to St. Thomas' proof that it assumes ideas and principles which are valid *within* the world, and then employs them with reference to the entire universe, thus assuming that they have validity *beyond* the world. To illustrate the point, we can inquire with respect to any object within the world, what is its location? but we cannot inquire what is the location of the world as a whole: we must beware of the "fallacy of transcendent inference." The newer form of the argument is less open to this criticism; for it first discloses an intramundane God, and then, by a second step, so to speak, elevates Him to a supramundane status.

41

The attitude of physicists to metaphysics

The criticisms of professional philosophers, such as Kant, have at all times received a great deal of attention from the exponents of natural theology, and have played an important part in reshaping the formulation of arguments. In contrast to this, contact between philosophers and men of science has been comparatively slight. The general attitude of physicists during the last two hundred years has been, that there is no need for them to know anything about metaphysics, whether it is a superstructure built on physics or not, since physical theories can be constructed, understood, and believed by anyone, whatever his philosophy. Newton, though profoundly interested in theology, seems to have held that the physicist can give his undivided attention to investigating the laws which will enable him to predict phenomena, and can leave the deeper problems entirely out of account: he can make it his purpose to describe rather than to explain. This was one of the implications of his celebrated declaration *hypotheses non fingo,*[1] and it determined the attitude of his successors: that is to say, men of science since Newton have generally held that correct (even if in some respects limited) knowledge regarding physics could be combined with any views whatever on the fundamental questions of Being and Reality; that part of the world could be rightly understood without reference to the whole; that natural philosophy was independent of metaphysics.

In a somewhat narrow sense this attitude can be justified: the fact cannot be disputed that great discoveries regarding the processes of the external world have been made by workers whose investigations in their field of research were not related in their own minds to any interest or belief outside it. But the effect of such a segregated way of thinking has been to make science a departmental affair, having no influence on life and thought except indirectly through its applications; and in recent years this isolationist attitude has weakened; partly from a desire to see science playing a greater part in life and thought; partly with a view to systematizing and perfecting the rough home-made metaphysics which is implicit in modern scientific writings; partly from a recognition that every branch of science depends on presuppositions which cannot be established by the methods of the science itself, and also that science deals with universals, which are proper

[1] *Principia, Schol. gener. sub finem*

objects of metaphysical study; and perhaps most of all, at any rate in recent years, from a hope that philosophy may help to clarify the mystery that wave-particles are the ultimate constituents of the universe.

Of existing philosophical systems, materialism does not as a rule make much appeal to physicists; for they see, perhaps more clearly than other people, the impossibility of explaining spiritual values in terms of protons and electrons.

It may further be said, that men of science are not naturally inclined to a monism of the opposite kind, namely subjective idealism; they are confident that reality exists independently of human cognition; for the achievement of mathematical physics is precisely this, that it has constructed a scheme of the universe which is trustworthy (that is, predictions based on it are always verified by experience), and which can be carried backward, still retaining its meaning and validity, to a time before the emergence of any sentient creature. Thus the physicists cannot bring themselves to disbelieve in the objectivity of the material world; and they have an instinctive sympathy with St. Thomas' rejection of the idealistic aspects of Neoplatonism, his conception of man as a part of Nature, his assertion of the meaning and value of the concrete things of sense, his reliance on experience, and his belief in the fundamental rationality of the universe. There is a natural affinity between science and the perennial philosophy: indeed, as we have seen, the line of descent of the modern physicist is to be traced not from the humanists of the Renaissance, but from the schoolmen of the twelfth and thirteenth centuries, who translated into Latin the Arabic versions of Greek mathematics and science.

It cannot be denied, however, that natural theology is not an altogether straightforward matter to the inquirer who has been trained in the ways of modern science. The aim of the present work has been to indicate—for the consideration of theologians who are not men of science—what the obstacles are, and to show—for the consideration of the scientific inquirer—that they are less formidable than has sometimes been supposed, and moreover, that the deeper understanding of the nature of the material universe, which has been achieved by scientific discovery, has opened up new prospects and possibilities to the advocate of belief in God.

Appendix

The Aristotelian defense of the maxim on motion

The Aristotelians met William of Ockham's objection (§ 14) by an argument which, in a modern form, would run somewhat as follows:

"Before the star X, in location A, moves to location B, X has not yet the perfection B. Therefore with regard to B it is in an imperfect state because it does not yet possess B: it is, in short, in potency to B. But that which does not already possess a certain perfection, cannot give to itself that perfection. *Nemo dat quod non habet.* Therefore the only alternative is that the perfection B, which X has not, is given to X by something which possesses that perfection actually; that is, X is moved to B by another. All movement is a passing from potency to act; and that which is in potency cannot pass from that state to the state of act except by something in act. A mover is in act *(nil agit nisi inquantum est in actu)* and the move is in potency (*nil patitur nisi inquantum est in potentia*); and since nothing can be both in act and in potency at the same time and in the same respect, therefore the mover cannot be identical with the moved."

To all this the Franciscan scholars could answer that a philosophy which is not founded on experience cannot possibly make assertions of any value about the actual behavior of material bodies in physical experiments; *a priori* reasoning is useless for the discovery of physical truth. Such a statement as "that which is in potency cannot pass from that state to the state of act, except by something in act" could be justified only by an induction based on extensive observations of the actual world for there is no *a priori* necessary reason for asserting it.

Moreover, there is in the Aristotelian reasoning a fallacy depending on the fact that in all these sentences, words are used in metaphorical senses. The concepts of "perfection" and "imperfection" have no relevance to the locations of a moving star: to talk about being "in an imperfect state because it does not possess B" is to introduce ideas which are foreign to the realities under discussion. The maxim *nemo dat quod non habet* presupposes the word *dat* to be used in its natural sense: if it is used in a metaphorical sense, the maxim is not necessarily true. When the Aristotelian speaks of "giving" a location, he is using the word "give" in a metaphorical sense (since a location is nothing but a relation to other bodies) and he is not entitled to use the maxim *nemo dat.* It is indeed absurd to suppose that a maxim such as this can tell us anything about the motion of stars in interstellar space; for the idea of "giving" is absent from the phenomenon.

The argument illustrates a fundamental vice of the Aristotelian method, namely the practice of regarding platitudes like *nemo dat* as if they were fundamental truths about Being, and applying them syllogistically to problems with which they have nothing whatever to do. The claim that verbal futilities such as these constitute a "supreme science," which ranks above the sciences that are based on observation and experiment, was rejected by the Ockhamists generally as preposterous.

Yet another objection to the argument of the Aristotelians related to their assertion that "nothing is at the same time and in the same respect both in potency and in act," which they represented as a consequence of the principle of contradiction. Their opponents could point out that the principle of contradiction relates only to *propositions:* it asserts that a proposition and its negation cannot both be true. Act and potency, however, are not propositions, but *conditions;* and the principle of contradiction does not assert that two *conditions* cannot co-exist; in fact, any number of examples of the simultaneous co-existence of conditions can be adduced. In order to prove that "nothing is at the same time and in the same respect both in potency and in act," it would be necessary first to *define* potency and act, and moreover it would be necessary to define them in terms of experiments or observations of operations performed on the external world, for in the new philosophy it was assumed as an axiom that assertions regarding the behavior of objects can be made only on the basis of actual observation; and unless this requirement has been fulfilled, the Aristotelians would not be justified in applying the notions of potency and act to phenomena in the external world. An induction from a further extensive series of experiments would then be necessary in order to prove the assertion about the impossibility of their co-existence.

One might further ask what, in the Aristotelian account of the free motion of a star, is to be regarded as the "mover." The fourteenth-century disputants were not under the necessity of answering this question, since they did not accept the law of inertia. Later Aristotelians, unable to ignore the difficulty, have contended that the star must have received an impulse at the Creation, and this impulse, which is still present in the star as it moves, is an instrument of the mover: the impulse is *in act* in the star, while the star is *in potency* to succeeding locations: thus the impulse is in fact the mover, so that the star does not move itself. To this argument it might be replied that the impulse is not *aliud,* something other than the star, but is part of the description of the state of the star: it is an attribute or quality or "accident" of the star itself; and this explanation cannot easily be fitted into the scheme of St. Thomas' concepts, as he describes them in the passage which was quoted in 6ξ § (pp. 117—19). In any case, if it is admitted that the "mover" may be no more than a mere accident of the "moved," the principle becomes inadequate to bear the weight of the argument for theism which is based on it.

Index